The Illustrated History
of
Phonographs

Daniel Marty

The Illustrated History
of
Phonographs

Dorset Press
New York

French edition copyright © 1979 by Daniel Marty and EDITA S.A. Lausanne

English edition copyright © 1981 by EDITA S.A.

Translation by Douglas Tubbs

This edition published 1989 by Dorset Press, a division of Marboro Books Corporation, New York

ISBN 0-88029-388-8

Printed and bound in Italy.

TABLE OF CONTENTS

Courtesy Antique Phonograph Monthly

TALKING MACHINES

Mankind has always sought means of perpetuating his brief passage on earth. First came the family saga, passed on by oral traditions; then the written word, followed by printing. Painting, and later, photography, proved a sure and lasting insurance against oblivion; but what of sound?

For hundreds of years men had dreamed of capturing and then releasing, the human voice, music and other sounds; but no technical means of doing so existed, and it was not until the nineteenth century that the dream came true. When this happened, significantly, it was a dreamer, a poet, who brought it about: in designing his 'mirror for sounds', the paleophone, Charles Cros brought the arts and the sciences together. The year 1877 marked an important step forward in the history of mankind. The principle that sounds are for ever changed many things. A few years yet would be required before talking machines became a practical proposition, and we can only regret that we cannot know the voice of Richard Wagner (who died in 1880), that of Victor Hugo (died 1885) or even, ironically enough, that of Charles Cros himself, who died in 1888.

An imaginary gramophone of 1632: sound contained in a sponge is given out when the sponge is squeezed. *'Le Courrier Véritable'*.

8

Historical Background

LITERARY SOURCES

François Rabelais (c. 1494-1553).

For twenty centuries and more there has been talk of reproducing the human voice. Various ingenious devices for imitating or amplifying the voice are described in history books about China, Greece and Ancient Egypt. To endow statues with speech, thus making them magic, divers primitive means were involved, including pieces of wood, bellows made of leather, or, simpler still, a person hidden inside, the voice being suitably distorted.

Rabelais, in the sixteenth century, was probably the first to describe means of conserving speech and reproducing it later. It was reasonable enough for a writer to draw a parallel between the preservation of foodstuffs by cold and the preservation of words the same way. Here is what he writes in Chapter LVI of *Pantagruel*, Book IV:

'The Skipper made answer; Be not afraid, my Lord, we are on the Confines of the Frozen Sea, on which, about the beginning of last Winter, happen'd a great and bloody Fight between the Arimaspians and the Nephelibates. Then the Words and Cries of Men and Women, the hacking, slashing and hewing of Battle-axes, the shocking, knocking and joulting of Armours and Harnesses, the neighing of Horses, and all other Martial Din and Noise, froze in the Air: And now the Rigour of the Winter being over, by the succeeding Serenity and Warmth of the Weather, they melt, and are heard.

By jingo, quoth Panurge, the Man talks somewhat like; I believe him; but cou'dn't we see some of 'em?

Here, here, said Pantagruel, here are some that are not yet thaw'd. He then throw'd us on the Deck whole handfuls of frozen Words, which seem'd to us like your rough Sugar-Plumbs, of many Colours, like those us'd in Heraldry, some words *Gules*, (This means also Jests and merry Sayings) some *Vert*, some *Azure*, some *Black*, some *Or*, (This means also fair Words;) and when we had somewhat warm'd them between our Hands, they melted like Snow, and we really heard them...

When they had been all melted together, we heard a strange Noise..., which the Pilot said, were the Noise made by the Charging Squadrons, the Shock and the Neighing of Horses.

Then we heard some large ones go off like Drums and Fifes, and others like Clarions and Trumpets. Believe me, we had very good Sport with them. I wou'd fain have sav'd some merry Odd Words, and have preserved them in Oil, as Ice and Snow are kept, and between clean Straw: But Pantagruel would not let me, saying, that 'tis a folly to hoard up what we are never like to want, or have always at hand, odd, quaint, merry and fat Words of *Gules* never being scarce among all good and jovial Pantagruelists.'

During the next century one finds, in *Le Courrier Véritable*, for April 1633, a description of a voyage by Captain Vosterloch to the South Seas. At one port of call this traveller found natives who used sponges for long-range communication. A message was spoken into the sponge and the latter sent off; the recipient had only to squeeze the sponge, and the words came out loud and clear. Not very scientific, perhaps, but a nice idea all the same.

Cyrano de Bergerac (1620-1655) imagined a machine not unlike a clock, but capable of storing words. This ancestor of the phonograph is described in his *L'Histoire comique des Etats et Empires de la Lune* (1650). Cyrano de Bergerac describes a box full of springs and things from which issued 'distinct and different sounds which with the great Moonmen do duty as a language'. A remarkable piece of seventeenth century *technologie* — but then Cyrano had already invented means of flying to the moon...

Cyrano de Bergerac (1619-1655).

Later, real phonographs found their way into print. Jules Verne worked them into the plot of *Les Tribulations d'un Chinois en Chine* (published 1879) and *Le Château des Carpathes* (1892).

Cavalcade de Nuits-St-Georges
Char de la Musique

At the turn of the century, the phonograph became so popular that it gave rise to this float, constructed for a carnival at Nuits-St-Georges in Burgundy.

THE SCIENTISTS

THOMAS YOUNG
(1773-1829)

Young's apparatus. It allowed sound to be seen but not heard. (1807).

'What man has done any man can do'. This was the motto of Thomas Young. To prove it he learned trick riding, and tight-rope walking as well. But athletics were only a beginning. Thomas Young, born at Milverton, Dorset, in 1773 was a polymath, a universal scholar. Having mastered Latin, Greek, French, Italian, Persian, Hebrew and Arabic, he took up botany, medicine and philosophy. Nor was his interest in any of these disciplines superficial. He made discoveries in the fields of Egyptology, medicine and physics. Thomas Young was also the first to represent graphically the vibrations from a source of sound. Here was the first step towards the invention of the phonograph. But there was, of course, still a long way to go. In 1807 Young wrote in his *Lectures on Natural Philosophy and Mechanics*: 'My instrument may be used to measure the number and amplitude of the vibrations emanating from sound-producing bodies when these are provided with a stylus capable of tracing a wavy line upon a turning cylinder. These vibrations may also be used, quite simply, to measure small intervals of time. If for example a body is made to vibrate at a certain frequency while the cylinder is turning and these vibrations inscribe themselves on the cylinder, the curve thus traced will give precise measurement of the time taken for part of a revolution, so that the movement of a given body may be related to the number of oscillations traced during the same period by the vibrating body'.

Upon a smoke-blackened drum, a stylus attached to a vibrating body would trace the latter's vibrations. There was no question as yet of inscribing words or music and it did not occur to Young to try and reproduce the tracings obtained. Young himself proceeded no further with these experiments, but mention may be made of certain other physicists who carried on his work without any basic alterations. The German scientist Weber, Duhamel of the Académie des Sciences, Wertheim and Lissajoux all contributed work on vibration traces. In 1857 another researcher appeared: Leon Scott.

LEON SCOTT
DE MARTINVILLE
(1817-1879)

Leon Scott's ambition was to produce an oral shorthand. Thomas Young's apparatus, even when improved by the workers mentioned above, provided no means of translating human speech into graphs.

Starting from the anatomy of the ear, Scott designed a device consisting of a horn (auricle) that terminated in a thin membrane (tympanum) the size of a shilling. At the centre of this membrane, on the outside, was fixed a hog's bristle. This was the world's first soundbox. A graph of the vibrations would be traced by the bristle on to a lamp-blacked glass cylinder.

The year 1857 was a crucial one for Scott:

— On 26 January, he lodged a sealed envelope with the *Académie*, containing the principles of *phonautography*, with details of a *phonautograph*.

— On 25 March, Patent No. 31470 was granted for a method of drawing or writing by sound, and for multiplying the result of this graphically with a view to industrial applications.

— On 16 November: Scott read a paper to the *Société d'encouragement* (corresponding to the British Association for the Advancement of Science) expounding the principles and applications of his invention. His talk was accompanied by a series of phonautographic illustrations.

Scott de Martinville (1817-1879), the inventor of the *phonautograph*.

Two years later, in 1859, Scott placed a contract with the German manufacturer, Rudolf Koenig, to market the *phonautograph*; he made no money from it, but his name at least goes down as a pioneer of the talking-machine.

Who then was this Leon Scott de Martinville? Although of good family (his grandfather was a baron) Leon was born without a silver spoon in his mouth; luck had deserted the previous generation, and as soon as he was old enough, the boy was apprenticed to a printer. Straight away he showed an interest in the books being printed, and soon he reached the stage of reading and correcting proofs. He was especially excited by the *Transactions* of the Académie des Sciences, and engineered opportunities to meet the scientists concerned. Soon the self-taught compositor was holding discussions with Ampère, Arago, Biot, Regnault and other great men. Probably the *phonautograph* idea came to him after reading *Traité de Physiologie* by Dr Longuet in 1853. The analogy between the human ear and the young printer's invention is obvious.

Much disheartened by Koenig's failure to exploit his invention, and with no resources apart from his meagre wage, Scott abandoned the exact sciences and turned to the history of art. He obtained a post with Firmin Didot, as librarian. Largely self-taught, Scott de Martinville wrote books on a variety of literary and scientific subjects, including: a working-man's criticism of novels and serials, a work on names, another on courtly romance and many others.

In 1877, on the invention of the phonograph, Scott claimed recognition of his own preliminary work which had made it possible. At that time he was dealing in prints from a stall in the yard behind No. 9 rue Vivienne, Paris. On 26 April, 1879, he died in Paris, a poor and forgotten man.

Scott de Martinville's *phonautograph* (1857).

CHARLES CROS (1842-1888)

Nadar's portrait of Charles Cros.

Gifted in too many directions to be taken seriously during his lifetime, Charles Cros was poet, chemist, physicist, painter and musician; too much perhaps for one man. Born at Fabrezan, not far from Carcassonne, on 1 October, 1842, Charles Cros was the fourth and last child of the family. His father, Henri Cros, a university professor with degrees in law and philosophy, moved to Paris in 1844. Five years later he was dismissed from the university because of his strongly republican views, and became a private tutor. He took charge of his son's education, and Charles obtained his *baccalauréat* in 1859.

Dutifully — and from financial necessity — he found work as an assistant master at the Institute for the Deaf and Dumb. Despite numerous vicissitudes he stuck it for three years, and even embarked on a study of medicine. On 23 February, 1863 a Ministerial decree put an end to his schoolmastering career. This was when young Charles took to *la vie de bohème*; alternating between literature and scientific research as the fancy took him, he also discovered the joys and temptations of Paris life.

In 1865 Charles Cros' talent for invention led him to design a telegraph system for Peru. Nothing came of this project; however, an automatic telegraph designed by him was shown at the Universal Exhibition of 1867.

Shortly afterwards he became interested in the photography of colours. His first publication was in fact a scientific treatise, *'solution générale du problème de la photographie des couleurs'* published in 1869 by Gauthier-Villars; not until four years later did his collected poems appear, under the name of *Le coffret de santal* (The Sandalwood Casket). A pattern was emerging. Spending much of his time in cafés frequented by artists and writers, Charles Cros met Verlaine, Rimbaud, Richepin and their set; but poetry did not monopolise his talent. On 16 April, 1877, he composed a letter to the Académie des Sciences, in Paris. Two days later he wrote on the envelope: 'packet containing description of a process for recording and reproducing phenomena perceived by ear, addressed to the Academy of Sciences on 18 April, 1877, by Charles Cros, 11 rue Jacob, Paris'. On 30 April the Academy officially accepted the packet, receipted by the signature of Monsieur Bertrand, numbering it 3109. The text enclosed ran as follows:

A PROCESS FOR THE RECORDING AND REPRODUCTION OF PHENOMENA PERCEIVED BY THE EAR

'Broadly, my process consists of obtaining a tracing of the oscillating membrane, and of using the tracing so obtained to reproduce the said motions

13

with their intrinsic relationships of duration and intensity upon the same membrane or upon another in such a way as to give back the sounds and noises which result from this series of motions.

It is my aim, therefore, to transform an extremely delicate tracing, such as that produced by delicate pointers moving over a smoke-blackened surface, to transform, I say, these traces into durable reliefs or hollows capable of driving a mechanism that will transmit these motions to an acoustic membrane. A light pointer forms part of the centre of a vibrating membrane; it terminates in a point (wire, barb or feather, etc...) which rests upon a smoked surface. This surface forms part of a disc which is caused to rotate and to move linearly at the same time. If the diaphragm is at rest the pointer will trace a plain spiral. If the diaphragm is vibrating, the spiral traced will be wavy, and these undulations will correspond exactly with all the oscillations of the diaphragm both in frequency and amplitude. The wavy and transparent spiral thus obtained is translated by accepted photographic means into a line of similar dimensions traced in relief upon, or carved into, a durable material such as hardened steel.

This done, the resulting disc is placed in a machine and made to revolve and move along at speeds similar to those of the recording surface. A metal point, if the line be incised (or a notched pointer if it be in relief) is pressed against the spiral by a spring. Moreover, the index carrying this point is integral with the centre of the face of the diaphragm designed to reproduce the sounds.

In these conditions this diaphragm will be animated not by vibrating air as before but by the wavy line guiding the needle, impulses exactly similar in frequency and amplitude to those which the recording diaphragm had undergone.

The spiral tracing represents succeeding equal intervals of time as lengthening or shortening lines. This is of no consequence so long as only the peripheral portion of the revolving circle is used, the turns of the spiral being very close together. But the central surface is wasted. In any case a helical track on a cylinder is much to be preferred and I am at present engaged in seeking practical means of production.'

Here, for all to read, are most of the elements necessary for building an apparatus able to record, and then to reproduce, sound. The use of photography in connection with the principles of the phonograph is not surprising when one remembers how interested Charles Cros was in the subject.

We are told that Cros having lodged a description with the Académie des Sciences, looked around for someone to build his apparatus. He failed to find anyone, and abandoned the attempt. However, a friend of his, the Abbé Lenoir, lent an attentive ear when Charles described his invention. The helpful cleric published an article about it (using the pseudonym Le Blanc) in *La Semaine du Clergé* for 10 October, 1877. This was the first use of the word 'phonograph' to describe a talking machine; hitherto it had signified something which described voices, sounds. Cros is also credited with the invention of the word *paléophone*, more poetic than phonograph; but his writings do not contain it.

Learning of Thomas A. Edison's work, Cros saw the danger of being forestalled by the American. Accordingly, he wrote to the Académie des Sciences

Caricature of Charles Cros illustrating the humorous poem *Le Hareng Saur.*

14

on 3 December, 1877, requesting that the packet lodged there some months previously, be opened and published forthwith in the *Transactions* of the Académie. This was done on the very same day.

Charles Cros was to write once more on this subject, following the demonstration by an Edison representative of a tin-foil phonograph to the Académie des Sciences in Paris on 11 March, 1878. This note of Cros' is as interesting as his letter of 16 April, 1877. First he acknowledges that Edison was the first person to reproduce the human voice; a proof that although Cros had invented and described such a machine he had never actually made one. The genuine admiration expressed in this letter shows how much Cros envied the practical outcome of Edison's work. The poet-inventor then sat down to analyse the process as demonstrated, drawing attention to the disadvantages of tinfoil, and suggesting the use of a gas-jet instead of a needle to follow the groove without wearing it out. More important still was his description of lateral recording as preferable to vertical — the 'hill and dale' method. This idea was to be picked up by Emile Berliner in 1887, although it did not come into its own until ten years after that.

After this note, which remained unpublished until 1970, Charles Cros wrote no more on the subject, disheartened perhaps at having been unable to get his machine built. We do not, unfortunately, possess a recording of Charles Cros' voice, but we do have a personal, indeed a vocal link — the comedian Coquelin the Younger, whom the poet first met in 1876. Cros wrote several vocal sketches or monologues for the brothers Coquelin, which became one of their specialities. The younger brother, Ernest, known as Coquelin the Younger and not yet a member of the Comédie Française, excelled in this specialised and largely forgotten art, and even wrote monologues himself under the name of Pirouette. Coquelin's repertoire included *l'Obsession, Le Bilboquet, L'Affaire de la Rue Beaubourg, la famille Dubois,* and even the poem *le Hareng Saur,* turned into a monologue. Poor Charles Cros made practically nothing from these texts while the actor declaiming them grew rich as he moved from one fashionable salon to another. This no doubt explains their frequent rows; but these soon blew over, both men being far too good-natured to harbour a grudge. In 1903 Coquelin the Younger, then aged 55, made two records for the *Gramophone Company*: *Le Hareng Saur* and *l'Obsession,* masterpieces by Charles Cros, whom absinthe had already assisted into the realm of legend.

Postage stamp commemorating the centenary of the invention of the phonograph.

15

During the Académie des Beaux-Arts meeting on 27 April
1889, Charles Gounod made a recording on an Edison
phonograph. Below: Thomas A. Edison in his study, 1905.

16

THOMAS ALVA EDISON
(1847-1931)

Thomas Alva Edison (1847-1931) listening to a recording being played on his *New Phonograph*.

In the phonographic hall of fame, Thomas A. Edison occupies a very special niche. He alone translated ideas into fact, marketed his invention and scored a world-wide success. What is more, this inventor cum tycoon amassed an enormous fortune, a highly unusual occurrence.

The origins of the Edison family were Dutch. In about 1730 they left the Zuider Zee, where they were millers, to seek their fortune in the Americas. They evidently succeeded quickly, for the inventor's great-grandfather was a banker. Life was not all plain sailing — it seldom was in the New World — but in 1828 we find a Samuel Edison marrying a schoolmistress of Scottish family named Nancy Elliot. This couple had three children: William Pitt, who became head of a tramway company, Tanine, who made a name as an author, and lastly Thomas Alva who was born on 11 February, 1847 at Milan, Ohio. Some years later the family moved to Michigan, settling at Port Huron.

Mrs Edison undertook the education of her children. Young Thomas quickly acquired a good knowledge of history and literature. He did not care much for mathematics but found chemistry enthralling. At twelve, asserting his independence and thirsting for adventure, he asked leave to sell newspapers on the trains between Port Huron and Detroit. After selling papers for a while, Edison decided to produce one himself, editing and printing it on the train for immediate sale to passengers. Today copies of the *Weekly Herald* are not to be found, but it would be interesting to see what was in them. Significantly, their raw material came over the telegraph; and when young Edison had to abandon his mobile journalism, he did not cut loose entirely, for he found work as a telegraphist, moving from one job to another and learning all the time. Telegraphy interested him; he read all the books he could find, experimented for himself and devised various improvements. His scientific education progressed. Edison is a perfect example of the self-made man.

With money earned by selling one of his inventions, Edison set up his own workshop when he was 22. Always methodical, he took out various patents which he either exploited or sold. His works rapidly outgrew the original premises at Newark, New Jersey. He moved to New York and then once more to the more salubrious atmosphere of Menlo Park, a hamlet near Elizabeth, N.J. Here, in spacious new premises, during the years 1875 to 1886 he settled down with a fine team of researchers and technicians to develop a great number of inventions, including the one which interests us here: the phonograph. It was natural perhaps in view of his work on telegraphs, electricity and telephones, that he should consider means of recording and reproducing sound. Perhaps too, the deafness which afflicted him early in life may have increased his interest in the science of communications. The precise date when the first Edison phonograph was built is not easy to establish, but we can at least sketch in the background.

While he was working on a device for automatically recording Morse code telegraph messages on a paper disc, it occurred to Edison that it might be possible to devise an apparatus that would record the spoken word. This took place in July 1877. Another recent invention had already caught his fancy, the telephone, and it seemed to him that one of its components, the diaphragm, offered further possibilities. Let the inventor take up the story:

'I had built a toy which included a funnel. The toy set in motion a pawl which formed part of a diaphragm and which, engaged with a cog-wheel, caused a pulley to turn. A string round this pulley was connected to a little cardboard figure of a man sawing wood. When someone sang «Mary had a little lamb» into the funnel, the little man started sawing. I thus reached the conclusion that if I could find a way of recording the movements of the diaphragm I could make the recorder reproduce the original movements imparted to the diaphragm by the person singing, and thus reproduce the human voice.'

Whether or not Edison was already familiar with the work of Charles Cros, it was on 29 November, 1877, that he handed one of his assistants, John Kruesi, a sketch of the apparatus required: the phonograph. As was his usual practice Edison offered a lump sum for the construction of the machine, in this case 18 dollars; if the workman did not fancy the deal, he could draw normal wages instead. In his diary another employee, Charles Batchelor, noted, under 4 December, 1877: 'Kruesi building the phonograph today', and two days later added: 'Kruesi finishing the phonograph'. Once again the nursery rhyme 'Mary had a little lamb' became the first test piece. In France it would have been *Frère Jacques* or *Sur le Pont d'Avignon...* So the world's first talking machine came to be built, at the beginning of December 1877. This first very crude machine consisted of a rotating cylinder covered with tin foil, and a diaphragm, but we may well imagine the joy with which its first spoken words were greeted.

Encouraged by this initial success Edison pressed on with development, but in the opposite direction to Cros. After experimenting with cylinders, Edison sketched plans for a clockwork phonograph using a foil-covered disc instead. This machine must have been built, but no example of it has survived.

Although far from perfect, Edison's phonograph created a worldwide demand. Some 600 were built, after the launching in 1878. Demonstrations were organised in the United States, then in England, and on 11 March, 1878, in Paris at a meeting of the Académie des Sciences with the Comte du Moncel in the chair. Edison's representative, Mr Puskas, gave an audition to the assembled Academicians. 'Monsieur Phonographe présente ses hommages à l'Aca-

Edison tin-foil phonograph, made by E. Hardy of Paris in about 1878. Hardy produced 500 models, which were quite successful.

An economical French machine on the Edison principle. Everything was made of wood, except the cylinder, which was of plaster.

démie des Sciences' he announced: then, when he had moved the cylinder back to its original position, a nasal, far away voice repeated the famous phrase. The men of science were enthusiastic, almost to a man. Only Dr Bouillaud was incredulous, talking darkly of a concealed ventriloquist. And this Jean-Baptiste Bouillaud was not just anyone: Balzac, who met him at old mother Vauquier's pension on the Montagne Sainte-Geneviève in Paris had put him in the novel *Le Père Goriot*.

After this, demonstration followed demonstration: on 15 March at the Société Française de Physique, 26 March at the Société d'Encouragement pour l'Industrie. Edison instructed his Paris agents, Messrs Puskas and Beet, to publicize the machine as much as possible. Thus a French newspaper for 24 August, 1878: 'The Phonography agency pursues its triumphal course. When one thinks that every evening and every afternoon the Salle des Capucines is as full as on the opening days, one wonders where this prodigious vogue for the most popular entertainment of 1878 will end. A new attraction is promised

Edison's phonograph was able to reproduce words. It can be seen that the recording diaphragm would also serve to play back the recording after a small horn was added. This model is the one that was demonstrated before the Académie des Sciences in 1878.

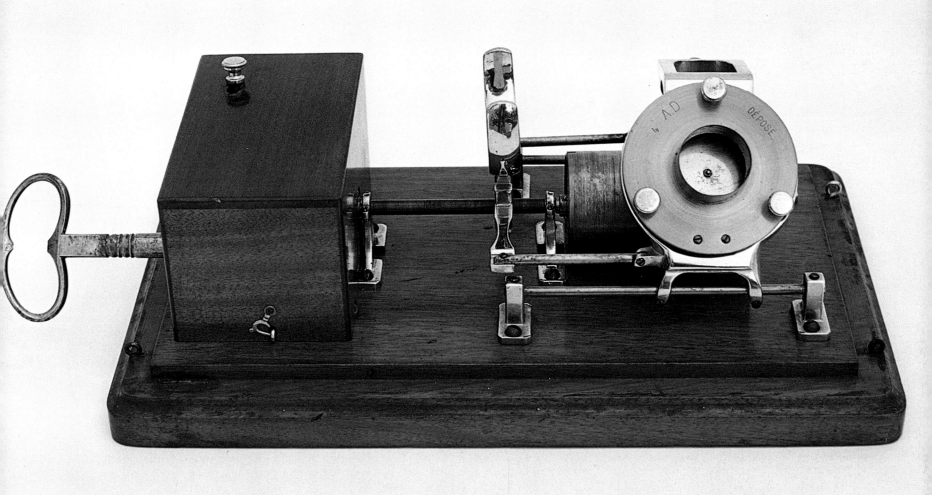

A curious French machine, in which the principle was identical to the Edison tin foil models but for two major differences: 1/ the brass cylinder which supported the tin foil was removable; 2/ a clockwork drive with a butterfly regulator drove the cylinder and the diaphragm. The letters 'A.D.' are the only clue to the manufacturer.

Edison's invention caught the imagination of chocolate manufacturer Besnier, who used it as a theme for his adverti

within the next few days.' The attraction was some sales gimmick, no doubt; it certainly was not 'hi-fi'!

After this whirlwind start the phonograph tended to mark time for ten years or so. Admittedly sound quality was poor. Certain syllables found difficulty in impressing the tin-foil sheet, especially those beginning with 'S'. The metal itself was noisy, and would not stand more than two or three playings. After that the diaphragm-point wore out the track and the sound became garbled. Thomas A. Edison meanwhile was busy on other matters, and he did not return to the phonograph until after the discovery by Sumner Tainter of a new material for cylinders, namely a hard wax composition, easy to impress but acoustically inert. After coming to terms with Tainter, Edison announced a new phonograph, with electric motor and wax cylinders, in 1887. That year also marked another stage in the company's development. From Menlo Park the factories were moved to West Orange, N.J. (which must have pleased Edison's Dutch ancestors): The works have now been turned into an Edison museum. The Menlo Park plant was removed in total by Henry Ford in the 1920's and shipped to Dearborn, Michigan, where it can be visited today in its original form. Thomas A. was not pleased with the new phonograph, and brought out an improved model in 1888. A new publicity drive followed. The machine appeared at all the important exhibitions of the period, and in particular the 1889 Exposition Universelle held in Paris to mark the centenary of the French Republic. This marked the real starting point of the Edison phonograph. Edison himself crossed the Atlantic and, as we shall see in another chapter, fascinated myriads of visitors to the Exhibition, who queued for hours to hear the 'magic' cylinders. Never, until 1929, was production of these phonographs halted. Each successive improvement brought an increase in sales. After 1889 the important dates in the story of the *Edison Phonograph* are as follows:

— 1908: Introduction of new cylinders, same format as previously but with double the playing time (4 minutes). These are called Amberol Cylinders.
— 1912: New material for cylinders introduced, made of unbreakable, rot-proof celluloid. These are called Blue Amberol Cylinders.
— 1913: Retaining the vertical ('hill and dale') cut, Edison introduced flat disc records: Edison Diamond Discs.

Care was taken to patent every improvement. There are therefore hundreds of Edison patents on the phonograph. He would sue at the drop of a hat, and the cases he won were to provide an excellent source of supplementary revenue.

The importance of Edison's inventions, his well-organised manufacture and effective sales techniques, not to mention the long production run (1878-1929) mean that collectors must devote a good deal of attention to Phonographs emanating, in the main, from West Orange.

When Thomas Alva Edison died, on 18 October, 1931, he bequeathed to the world a famous name, and to his heirs a substantial fortune, a proof that one inventor at least was not deficient in business sense.

Edison in about 1890.

Following Edison's principles, small manufacturers made tin foil phonographs, some of which were to be used in schools for practical lessons.

Growth of the Industry in the United States and of its European Branches

Tainter demonstrated his *Graphophone* at the Paris Exposition Universelle in 1889.

◄ The best-known *Graphophone*, the model *B*, known as the *Eagle* as its price was 10 dollars, and the ten-dollar piece of that time carried an American Eagle on the reverse.

GRAPHOPHONE AND COLUMBIA

Already famous as inventor of the telephone, Alexander Graham Bell (1847-1922) was awarded the Prix Volta for his work by the Académie des Sciences in Paris in 1880. The substantial sum which accompanied this prize was immediately used by Dr Bell to establish the VOLTA LABORATORY ASSOCIATION, devoted to electrical and acoustical research, at Washington, DC. As partners in this enterprise Bell chose his cousin Chichester Bell, who came over from England, and a physicist, Charles Sumner Tainter. On 28 February 1880, Bell and Tainter lodged a sealed envelope containing descriptions of their early work on phonographs. The following year they turned their attention to jets of compressed air as a means of playing their records, but with no real success. One problem remained unsolved: the material on which their recordings were made gave only mediocre sound quality. After much experiment Chichester, Bell and Tainter hit upon the idea of covering cardboard cylinders with wax. This marked an important step forward in the history of the phonograph.

The new device was patented in the U.S.A. on 4 May, 1886. Patent No. 341.214 did not employ the term 'graphophone', although that word was already in existence, the VOLTA GRAPHOPHONE COMPANY having been founded that year. A second company, for manufacturing the machines at Bridgeport, Conn., was launched, called the AMERICAN GRAPHOPHONE COMPANY.

Thomas A. Edison's first reaction was to complain that someone had stolen his invention; but because he needed Tainter's improvements there was no lawsuit. The two concerns therefore went ahead with the technical development of their respective machines, but marketing was not yet organised. Then a businessman, Jesse H. Lippincott, came on the scene, realising how much there was in it for him. He brought the two rivals together and became commercial representative of both EDISON and GRAPHOPHONE, founding on 14 July, 1888, the NORTH AMERICAN PHONOGRAPH COMPANY.

Lippincott remained in charge for only two years, during which time he mistakenly encouraged the use of phonographs to replace shorthand-writers. Office use was not enough to make the talking-machine famous. A second campaign was therefore launched: automatic phonographs operated by putting money in a slot. The financial return from 'penny in the slot' machines in public places was excellent. Their publicity value was equally great; but the principal sales promoters were the cylinders themselves — music, that is to say, and the artists who recorded.

The management of the COLUMBIA PHONOGRAPH COMPANY took over and came to the assistance of Bell's AMERICAN GRAPHOPHONE COMPANY. Much effort went into the compilation of a catalogue of recordings, and the stage was set for a phonograph boom.

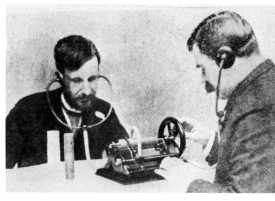

Charles Sumner Tainter listening to a *Graphophone*.

The reproduction of cylinders by moulding still lay ten years in the future when, in 1891, large scale marketing was decided upon. Thus, musicians and singers had never had it so good. Despite ingenious arrangements for running several recording-phonographs at once, performers still had to spend hours at a time playing and re-playing the same piece.

Following results from the sale of coin-operated machines, the GRAPHO-PHONE COMPANY set itself another task: to conquer the family market. The first phonographs having been expensive, it was necessary to design a simple new model within reach of the average household. At Christmas 1897 the machine went on sale, at a price of ten dollars. This sum was symbolic: the U.S. ten-dollar gold piece in those days was known as an Eagle from the American eagle on the reverse. So publicity for the new phonograph was based on the fact that it cost no more than ten dollars, and it was called, naturally enough, *The Eagle*.

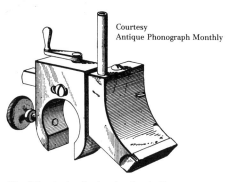

Courtesy
Antique Phonograph Monthly

The launching of this model was to result in world-wide sales. To make these spectacular developments possible profound modifications had been made to the parent companies, GRAPHOPHONE and COLUMBIA. The registered offices were moved from Washington, D.C., to New York City, although Columbia, the name of the Federal capital district, was retained for reasons of prestige. One of the company's trademarks, too, was the figure of a woman dressed in red,

The 'Simplex' cylinder shaving knife.

Cylinder Graphophones

ON the other hand, there is a large section of the public which chooses the cylinder machines and records because the prices range somewhat lower, the cyinder records are cheaper, and, above all, because

With Cylinder Graphophones only, Records of the Voice, or of any Sound, can be easily made at Home and Immediately Reproduced.

NOTHING is more delightful than to have a " VOICE ALBUM "—a collection of the voices of yourself, your family and friends. This is far more interesting than photography and less expensive, while it affords an endless source of amusement in the home.

Blank cylinders for making records at home are sold in felt-lined boxes, in which they may be permanently kept if desired.

These are made in two sizes:

Napkin Ring, (shaved) 10 cents each,
Medium (P) (shaved) 20 cents each

Courtesy Antique Phonograph Monthly

An extract from the Columbia Graphophone catalogue, 1906.

26

One of the rare *Graphophones* equipped with a mandrel capable of playing Stentor cylinders. The model *AG* was also known as the *Columbia Grand*.

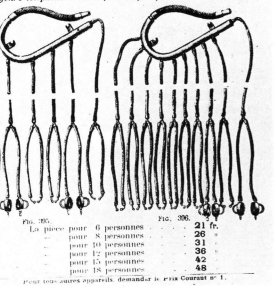

Extract from the 1899 catalogue of the Etablissements Pathé Frères, which then distributed *Graphophones* and their accessories. It is open at the page showing tubes and earphones. The *Graphophone* No. 75 corresponded to the *AT* model.

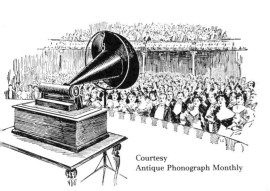

Courtesy
Antique Phonograph Monthly

The *Graphophone* entertaining an audience.

Automatic Graphophone BS. An *Eagle* apparatus encased in glass and wood, here equipped with earphones. The weight of a coin started the machine.

white and blue and holding the Star-Spangled Banner. Branch offices were opened in leading provincial cities: Baltimore, Chicago, Buffalo, St Louis, etc. and these were followed by European headquarters in London and Paris.

Without dropping its earlier models the AMERICAN GRAPHOPHONE COMPANY turned out thousands of the new EAGLE for the family market from the plant in Bridgeport, Connecticut.

The possibility of making one's own records was an added attraction, but the main fascination for owners of a graphophone was listening to one's favourite performers whenever one wished. As the catalogue put it: 'Possession of a Graphophone makes it possible, at modest cost, to keep up to date with the latest operatic and musical comedy successes, with concert singers of the highest renown, to hear the voice of a noted comedian reciting some of his side-splitting monologues. The Graphophone is to the ear what the camera is to the eye; superior, in fact to a camera because it is Simple and Instantaneous, recording and reproducing on the spot, with utmost fidelity anything it is allowed to hear.'

The Company's development was spectacular, but when flat records proved a serious rival to cylinders, the change-over was rapid. Manufacture of disc-playing gramophones proceeded side by side with that of cylinder GRAPHO-PHONES. But let us conclude the story of COLUMBIA cylinders. The advent of moulded cylinders (1901) produced a boom in industrialisation. To cater for customers abroad, factories were opened in various countries where recordings could be taken and mouldings made of the work of popular local artistes. Paris became an important manufacturing centre for COLUMBIA cylinders. The phonographs themselves were imported and distributed by the COLUMBIA PHON-OGRAPH CO. GEN'L, 34 Boulevard des Italiens, Paris.

An improvement brought in as a result of competition from Edison was the manufacture by Columbia of indestructible cylinders. Thomas B. Lambert ceded his patent relating to moulded celluloid cylinders on a cardboard core reinforced by a metal ring at each end. These cylinders went on sale in 1907, price 35 cents. Having preceded Edison in the use of celluloid, COLUMBIA were shortly to follows his lead in 1909 when they increased the playing time of their cylinders to 4 minutes (price 50 cents). Despite these strenuous efforts, Columbia proved unable to prolong production of cylinders beyond July 1912. On that date they gave up making cylinders, but they went on making their discs and phonographs as they had done since the turn of the century.

The first cylinders of C.S. Tainter in 1885 had been 15 centimetres long and 3.5 centimetres in diameter. Jesse H. Lippincott's incursion into office machinery had the merit of standardizing sizes of GRAPHOPHONE and EDISON cylinders, which could be played interchangeably on both companies' machines. There were only three sizes of cylinder:

'G', for 'Grand', 'Home Grand' and 'Columbia Grand'
'C', for 'Universal Graphophone'.
'P' for all other cylinder Graphophones

It was in the last-named size that 'indestructible' cylinders were made.

Diaphragm details of the *Graphophone BC*, shown on the opposite page.

The *Graphophone, Universal C* type, was one of the first recording machines for office use. The unusually long cylinder should be noticed which, combined with the slow rotation of 80 rpm enabled fairly long letters to be recorded.

Side view of the *Graphophone BC*.

Thanks to its size, to its three-spring clockwork motor, and above all, to its giant diaphragm (11 cm — 4.3 in — diameter), the *BC* model was known as 'The Premier' or the *Graphophone du XXe siècle*. The first of these machines appeared on the market in about 1906.

Graphophone type N, made about 1895. The head office of the American Graphophone Co. was still at Washington at that time. Apart from Bell and Tainter patents, the machine was also covered by Mac-Donald's patent of 16 October 1894. The Werner Brothers, of Paris, looked after the distribution of this American machine in France.

The Graphophone AQ model, a popular and economic cylinder phonograph. The movement of the playing head is controlled by a fork resting on an endless screw; the aluminium diaphragm gave good sound quality.

Above: This *Graphophone* could take Stentor cylinders, but its motor was weak. In Europe it was known as the *Double-Eagle*, but its official name was *Model AB.*

Above right: Detail of the type *N*: the identifying plate carries the origination.

The diaphragm of the *Graphophone* type *BK* was contained in a metal frame shaped like a lyre. There are certain similarities between it and the Edison system. Below: Detail of the diaphragm.

This small phonograph (26.5 x 19 x 24 cm —
10.4 x 7.4 x 9.4 in) marked the beginnings of
more elaborate ornamentation by the Graphophone company's cabinet-makers. Dating from
1901, the AA model was notable for the introduction of aluminium in the mechanism.

Another version of the *Eagle*. The garland trademark was complemented by a representation
of Columbia draped in the star-spangled banner.

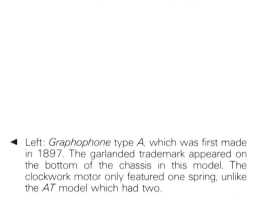

◄ Left: *Graphophone* type *A*, which was first made
in 1897. The garlanded trademark appeared on
the bottom of the chassis in this model. The
clockwork motor only featured one spring, unlike
the *AT* model which had two.

The type *QQ* was known as the *Mignon* in France,
and was the great success for the Graphophone
company, after the *Eagle*. As the name suggested,
these were small phonographs of modest price.
This model was much imitated in Germany (see
Excelsior, Angelica).

Foreseeing the probable ascendancy of the lateral-cut discs placed on the American market by the GRAMOPHONE COMPANY, the GRAPHOPHONE COMPANY'S directors behaved very wisely. Realising that they had to fight on the same ground, and unencumbered by scruples, they found ingenious ways round the relevant VICTOR and GRAMOPHONE patents and brought out disc-players on exactly the same lines. The year 1901 saw the earliest DISC GRAPHOPHONE, which was followed by a wide and imposing range of models in subsequent seasons. Record sizes were cribbed from Victor: 6¾ in and 10 in diameter (17 cm and 25 cm). Production of the two systems, cylinders and discs side by side meant that disc-Graphophones were not very numerous in the early years of their production; but they were handsome machines and they had a good tone. The cessation of cylinder manufacture in 1912 did not affect the company's other activities.

DISC GRAPHOPHONES

The American Graphophone Company produced ▶ disc-playing machines after 1902. The sound box made playing simple. The horn was nickle-plated brass in a flower shape.

This machine is identical to the *Columbia AU*. It was sold by the Standard Talking Machine Co. The only difference was that the turntable was bigger, so that larger discs had to be used, with a central hole of 1.4 cm (0.5 in) diameter. These discs were sold for 60 cents each, while the smaller Columbia records cost 1 dollar.

The *Columbia* type *AU* was easily folded away, and was fitted with a carrying handle. The horn support was in aluminium. The horn itself, although American, was not of the same make as the machine.

The large painted floral horn mounted over a ▶ mahogany cabinet gave this rather expensive *Columbia* machine an elegant look.

The *Columbia AK* was built along the same lines as the previous model, except that the horn was lightly made of aluminium.

CARUSO · RENAUD · MELBA
A L'OPÉRA

TOUS LES JOURS
AU
GRAMOPHONE
ENTREZ
LES ÉCOUTER

IL Y A BIEN DES MACHINES PARLANTES
MAIS IL N'Y A QU'UN SEUL
GRAMOPHONE

GRAMOPHONE

Emile Berliner was the main force behind the perfection of the flat disc with lateral zig-zag recording. He created the Gramophone trademark.

The Compagnie Française du Gramophone advertisement put its emphasis on the famous
◄ artistes that recorded for them. The French baritone Maurice Renaud has been promoted to the same rank as the two superstars Caruso and Melba.

The history of this make is most interesting and deserves to be told in detail. Invention played a relatively minor rôle in the evolution of the *Gramophone*, because it was a question rather of painstaking refinement of existing processes and, once satisfactory models had been built, of fantastic publicity through prestigious recordings. Good sales organisation and a rapidly growing network of factories in all the major countries quickly established the GRAMO-PHONE COMPANY as a world leader, and obliged rival concerns to adopt its systems or go out of business.

Invariably, at the bottom of every late nineteenth century industrial undertaking there is one man. In this case, that man was born in Hanover in 1851 and his name was Emile Berliner. Reaching the United States very young, he tried many jobs including that of secretary. His various jobs led him from New York to Washington. The young man was interested in science, and spent his evenings reading in the public libraries. With his modest savings, Berliner set up a little laboratory and conducted experiments. His first work concerned telephones, newly invented by Alexander Graham Bell. Returning briefly to Europe, Berliner, with his brother Joseph, started a factory for the manufacture and marketing of telephones. The TELEPHON FABRIK BERLINER at Hanover was before long to prove of crucial importance in the history of the GRAMO-PHONE COMPANY. When Berliner returned to Washington in 1883 he began patiently probing into the phonograph and its origins. Starting from a study of the Phonautograph, Scott de Martinville's device, then the writings of Charles Cros, in which the two possibilities of recording on disc or cylinder are propounded, Berliner became interested in the patents taken out by Edison in 1878 and finally began work on the discoveries of Bell and Tainter. Possibly to avoid clashing with established processes, Berliner focused his attention on the flat disc, which seemed to him full of promise.

The importance of Emile Berliner's work concerns the recording of sound by laterally cut grooves on a flat disc. By 1887 his process was in use. It was known as Phonogravure. Instead of tin foil as used by Edison, Berliner employed a circular zinc plate lightly coated with wax. The recording stylus scratched away the wax leaving the metal exposed; the plate was then placed in an acid bath, which attacked the metal where it was not protected by wax. In other words Berliner made etchings of the human voice.

A demonstration was held at the FRANKLIN INSTITUTE in Philadelphia in May 1888. The results were satisfactory but not yet suitable for exploitation on a commercial scale. Emile Berliner continued his experiments, and before long

The most famous of the *Gramophones*: accompanied by the terrier Nipper, it symbolised His Master's Voice. The vertical winding handle made this model easy to recognise. Curiously enough, the machine had a different name according to country, although it was common to all the branches of the company. In France it was known as the *Gramophone No. 3*, in the U.S.A. as the Model *B*, made by Eldridge B. Johnson, while in Canada it appeared as the *Berliner Standard Gram-o-phone* type *A*.

Apart from a small, hand-powered phonograph which was only a toy, the first machine in the series was this one. There were three versions, of which the machine illustrated was the simplest. The motor, mounted on a base, was exposed. This model was withdrawn from the market fairly rapidly.

Above: Details of the *Victor Monarch* and its 'Exhibition' diaphragm.

Left: This *Victor Monarch* was built around 1904 in the United States. The joining arm between the horn and the diaphragm is in brass and the playing arm steel.

The card shows the fascination the phonograph inspired. It was a most sought-after gift.

The automatic *Gramophone* was designed for public entertainment, and played after being fed with 10 centime pieces.

The model seen here was a little larger than the Gramophone symbol. The machine was sold in the United States in 1901 under the name *Victor* type *C*. In France, it was sold by the Compagnie Française du Gramophone.

Monarch No. 7 of 1903 with wooden support and large nickled horn.

43

Publicity that appeared in May 1903 in *Musica*. Jean de Reske, who did not record for *Gramophone*, pointed out the merits of the make. He was joined on the page by Sarah Bernhardt, Francisque Delmas and Aïno Ackte, who had all made a few recordings. Rivalled by Pathé, who sold their phonographs and cylinders through a credit sales house, Girard et Cie, the Gramophone Company sold its machines through Tallendier, in Paris. Having arrived rather late on the market, the Gramophone Co. did not break through by credit sales, but by the high artistic quality of its recordings.

◄ Left: The large floral horn on the *Monarch No. 13* was typical of Gramophone products.

succeeded in taking electrotype copies from his discs, which paved the way to their reproduction commercially. The phonograph used by Berliner was primitive in the extreme, operated by turning a handle, with a ball governor to hold the speed constant. Crude as it was, the machine was christened *Gramophone*, to distinguish it from Edison's *Phonograph* and the *Graphophone* of Bell and Tainter; it may well have been the toy-like simplicity of his machine that gave Berliner the idea of manufacturing a toy gramophone during one of his trips home to Germany. These toys were produced for some years, probably from 1889 to 1891. The firm of Kämmerer and Reinhardt, of Watershausen produced children's records in several European languages under Berliner patents; but this can hardly be regarded as the starting point of the *Gramophone*. Once back in America, Emile Berliner found ways of improving his records and the means of taking copies. The first commercial flotation was the UNITED STATES GRAMOPHONE COMPANY, with offices at 1410 Pennsylvania Avenue, Washington, D.C., but without enough capital for rapid expansion.

However, an event of first importance occurred during 1893: a young man joined Berliner's concern, Fred Gaisberg by name. Having worked for some while with the COLUMBIA PHONOGRAPH COMPANY, Gaisberg understood the technique of recording; what is more, he was an excellent pianist, a fact which was to stand him in good stead. The first records he was concerned with were: 1) *The Lord's Prayer*, spoken by Berliner himself in a guttural voice and a heavy German accent, and 2) The *Mocking-Bird* whistled by John York Atlee 'accompanied by Professor Gaisberg'. Primitive perhaps, but what collectors' pieces!

The quality of the recordings improved but the little hand phonographs did not really satisfy their audience. Originally the nominal speed of rotation was 70 revolutions per minute, but it was not easy to prevent variations in pace. Gaisberg therefore decided to call in a specialist and fit a clockwork motor to his talking-machines. A young man named Eldridge Reeves Johnson (1867-1945) was found, with workshops at Camden, N.J. It was from here that the first gramophone motors emerged. By now Berliner had found the necessary capital, and was at last able to launch the gramophone on a proper scale. This was at the end of 1896.

Here it is worth remarking that the dynamic qualities of the team Berliner had built up were largely due to their age. Gaisberg was young, Johnson 29, Berliner himself an energetic 45. Starting from the bottom of the social ladder these men all made large fortunes and reached the top. They became '*Gramophone* millionaires' — and they were by no means the only ones...

With more sophisticated machines and much improved records made of ebonite the *Gramophone* was poised to take the world by storm. In the United States branches had been opened in New York and Philadelphia and recording studios set up. The lateral engraving process had proved a great success, although it had one disadvantage vis à vis the cylinder system: it was not possible for *Gramophone* users to make their own recordings. Sales, therefore, had to be based on other considerations. This was where Fred Gaisberg came in once more. Everything, he reasoned, would depend upon assembling an attractive catalogue. He practised what he preached, travelling the world in search of

The *Monarch No. 15* case was elaborately decorated, and matched the wooden horn. ►
The 30 cm (11.8 in) turntable was designed to accept the same size *Monarch* records that came out in 1903.

A *Monarch* sold by the Belgian subsidiary of the Gramophone and Typewriter Co. It had a rather unusual brass horn. The inlaid plaque in the case carried the series number, 91094, and the original 'Recording Angel' trademark.

celebrities, and personally recording their voices: Adelina Patti, Dame Nellie Melba, Caruso, Chaliapin... all the great names of grand opera and the concert platform, even the choir of the Sistine Chapel in St Peter's, Rome.

Meanwhile subsidiary companies were floated, in England (1898), then in France, Germany and elsewhere. This proved the big moment for Emile Berliner's brother Joseph, whom we left in charge of the TELEPHON FABRIK BERLINER at Hanover. This works now became the largest record factory in the world, pressing discs for the entire European market. The original of every recording made by the globe-trotting Fred Gaisberg was sent to Hanover, where all matrices were made from which the millions of records were pressed. Another press works was set up at Riga in Latvia on the Baltic, although records were never made there on a similar scale.

The *Gramophone* technology evolved by Berliner and his team over a space of ten years was never changed; it was simply improved in 1925 by the advent of electrical recording. Although a late starter in the talking machine stakes, *Gramophone* outstripped all its competitors.

Never was a company more publicity conscious. The slogan 'It pays to advertise' might have been invented by Gaisberg himself, although he would

An unflattering caricature as an ape of Enrico Caruso, the lyrical star of *His Master's Voice* recordings.

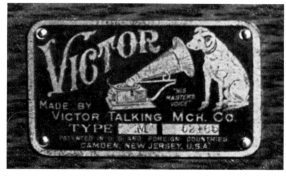

Victor III identifying label.

A *Victor III* with the 'Exhibition' sound box and diaphragm, of about 1904. The horn, in painted sheet metal and brass, was very American, and not found in Europe.

The *Gramophone No. 4A* was provided with an unusual system on the playing arm in 1903, which only lasted for a short time. The diaphragm was fixed to the arm by an axle. To lift the needle from the groove, the diaphragm was turned over on its axis and rested with the needle upwards on the arm.

The *Gramophone Monarch Junior* had a nickle-plated brass horn of 32 cm (12.5 in) diameter.

Right: A German-made *Gramophone* with a simpler wood horn and of smaller size.

The *Monarch No. 15* was powered by three large springs, which enabled several record sides to be played without rewinding. The tonality of the wooden horn was extremely good.

have been more likely to say, in the idiom of the time, 'Boost for Gramophones!' We have already noted the importance given to performers' names in the record catalogue. Prominence was given to famous composers and instrumentalists: Massenet, Jean de Reszké, Paul Mounet, Reynaldo Hahn, Diemer, Ernest Reyer and Raoul Pugno. Composers were specially commissioned to write pieces for the gramophone, the best known of which became Leoncavallo's *Mattinata* sung by Enrico Caruso, accompanied by the composer at the piano.

But the real stroke of genius came from London, where the GRAMOPHONE COMPANY had recently been formed.

Francis James Barraud, whose family was of Huguenot extraction, was born in London on 16 June, 1856. He studied art and developed into a very respectable painter. One day in 1899 he painted a dog listening to records. 'If only poor Nipper were alive he could have sat for me' he mused, but his terrier had died in 1895. Barraud found an old photo. That is how Nipper was to become, *post mortem*, the most famous dog in the world. Barraud had now to find a machine for he never worked without a model. He chose an *Edison Bell*. When he had finished his picture he offered it to the Edison people. Nothing came of this (of all the wasted opportunities...!) Barraud next contacted the GRAMOPHONE COMPANY. Barraud was received by Barry Owen, head of the English operation, who agreed to purchase the picture on condition, naturally, that a record-playing GRAMOPHONE should replace the cylinder machine.

No agreement was reached there and then, but after an exchange of letters and telegrams the matter was settled on 15 September, 1899. A day or two later, the Company delivered a *Gramophone* and Francis Barraud set to work, complaining that no records had come with the machine. This was fair enough, for how without one could Nipper recognise His Master's Voice?

Emile Berliner was shown the picture; he was impressed and took a copy home with him in May, 1900. The agreement assigning the copyright in 'His Master's Voice' was dated July 1900, but by this time Berliner's business affairs were going badly. Eldrige Johnson took them over, and was shortly to float the VICTOR TALKING MACHINE COMPANY, with the listening dog as its trademark. Barraud's picture was used in advertising and on the machines themselves; it did not appear on record labels until 1909 in Europe. Francis Barraud received £ 50 for his painting and another £ 50 for the copyright; but he also got many orders from GRAMOPHONE COMPANY (VICTOR in the U.S., THE GRAMOPHONE COMPANY in Britain, and later of course, HIS MASTER'S VOICE and H.M.V.) for replicas of his picture, which made him a lot of money. He died in 1924, leaving no great name as a painter, but one work which was famous all over the world. There are photographs of Francis Barraud but so far as is known, no record was ever made of his voice.

Sales of records and *gramophones* continued to mount. Gradually *gramophones* lost their external horns as these became part of the instrument, around 1906. This in no way interfered with the sound, but it did have a profound effect on the gramophone as a piece of furniture. Nowadays, the financial structure of the group stemming from the GRAMOPHONE COMPANY is entirely altered; but the famous dog trademark is very much alive.

Courtesy
Antique Phonograph Monthly

Victor Monarch with antique hand-carved cabinet, price 150 dollars.

◀ The American *Victor 1*, a small *Gramophone* with a floral horn sold in France in about 1909.

A classic *Monarch Junior* gramophone with a nickle-plated brass horn. The motor had only one spring, which allowed one side to be played before rewinding.

Left: Another *Monarch Junior* with an extremely rare aluminium horn. It was almost certainly of French make.

Left: It seems that this machine was never made by the European subsidiaries of the Gramophone Co., but only by the Victor Co. in America. However, its low price and compact horn gave it a world-wide popularity and it was distributed in many countries.

Louis Lumière registered several patents from 1909 for a ▶ pleated paper diaphragm, but it was not until 1924 that His Master's Voice sold the diaphragm under license. The large diaphragm was fragile but very musical. Below: An unusual papier mâché horn that was painted to imitate wood, and mounted on a French-made *Monarch* gramophone.

A chromo showing the pleasures a phonograph could bring. There was another version of this illustration showing an Edison phonograph with a floral horn.

54

EDISON

The phonographs built by Thomas Alva Edison are the perfect reflection of American industry, both in conception and method. After the initial essays at recording on tin-foil, some short runs of demonstration machines were built. These are the incunabula of the phonograph. Fortunately examples of these tin-foil phonographs exist in museums, so that collectors can admire what they cannot possess.

In France these machines were marketed by E. Hardy, but in small numbers. Working on the same principle, other makers copied Edison's model, e.g. *Fondain* and *Ducretet*, in Paris. Edison, however, knowing full well that tinfoil recordings would never be a commercial proposition, took no action, having other things on his plate. C.S. Tainter's important discovery (wax-covered cylinders) rekindled Edison's interest, but once again early models proved disappointing, and large scale production was postponed. Designed in 1887 at the new West Orange factory, this machine was driven by a battery-powered electric motor; it was quickly replaced by the famous Model M, also electrically driven, which marks the true beginning of the talking machine industry. With the formation in July 1888 of the NORTH AMERICAN PHONOGRAPH COMPANY (one month before the death of Charles Cros) the industry was off to a good start. Several handicaps had yet to be overcome before the phonograph was ready for world-wide marketing. The design had to be changed; it was very heavy and tricky to use; the price was too high, and the whole design required alteration as the machine was intended for office use rather than amusement. Edison made a close study of the market and came to the following conclusions:

1. It was easier to use clockwork than an electric motor;

2. A range of models should be offered, varying in price and presentation;

3. The phonograph would find many applications and there should be a suitable type for each. Public and private listening were mentioned, stenographic use, and coin-in-the-slot operation, with machines known as 'coin-slot phonographs'.

In 1896 Edison announced his first clockwork machine, costing 100 dollars. The improvements incorporated in this *Edison Spring Motor Phonograph* entailed also a change of name. It became the *Triumph*. The next phonograph from West Orange was the *Home*, of 1896, which was produced until 1913. There were seven versions, price 40 dollars. The *Standard* announced in 1898, as the name implies, was a popular model at a medium price — 20 dollars; it too was made in seven versions and continued until 1913. Edison hit the mark with this model, which is still the most widely distributed, and therefore the commonest and least expensive.

To compete against cheap models from the opposition, especially the *Graphophone Eagle*, Edison produced the *Gem*, a very simple little phonograph which underwent improvement over the years. Manufacture commenced in 1899 and ceased in 1913 along with that of all phonographs with external horn, the *School* model excepted.

The Edison oak desk for phonograph and typewriter.

The three models just mentioned: the *Home*, *Standard* and *Gem* sold in huge quantities. Each model underwent successive improvements as these came out: cylinders of two-minutes duration at first, then four minutes; diamond sound-boxes on *Home* and *Standard*, and swan-neck horns (except on the *Gem*). These models were sold all over the world, which was not the case with all the models from West Orange.

A noteworthy member of the phonograph range with external horn was the *Edison Concert* launched in 1899 and playing Stentor cylinders. Versions of the *Concert* with electric drive are called *Opera* (running from a 2 volt battery) and *Oratorio* (from 110/110 volt mains supply). The corresponding coin-operated machines were called *Climax*, *Ajax* and *Vulcan*.

At the upper end of the range from 1907 and 1911 we find the *Idelia* early versions playing two-minute cylinders, later models (from 1908) taking four-minute cylinders as well. Not many of these de luxe instruments were sold.

Stemming directly from the *Standard*, the *Fireside* model came out in 1909, playing initially both types of cylinder but in Model B form the four-minute only. Designed to replace the *Standard*, the *Fireside* had little success and therefore is less common than the predecessor, although the latter was made for only four years.

The *Edison Opera Phonograph* was the last machine to have an external horn if one excludes the *School Phonograph* of specialised application. Produced for less than two years (1911-1913) it is the only Edison made with a stationary sound-box; the cylinder travelling across. Only four-minute records could be played. In October 1912 this model became known as the *Edison Concert Phonograph*.

Certainly Thomas A. Edison, once his mind was made up, remained loyal to his carefully planned programme — pig-headed might be a better word. The West Orange plant went on producing cylinders until 1929. The fashion for floral horns gradually died out. The VICTOR company, closely followed by COLUMBIA in 1906, housed the trumpet inside the cabinet, compelling Edison to do the same: his *Amberola Phonographs* were called after the four-minute cylinder. A whole series of internal-horn machines was produced, gradually

Right, above and below: When he restarted work ▶ on the phonograph in about 1887, Thomas Edison, who had been stung into continuing the development by the inventions of Tainter, the wax cylinder and the 'floating stylus,' made a new machine powered by an electric motor driven by batteries. He soon dropped this model to manufacture the *Class M*, which was the model that he exhibited at the 1889 Paris Exposition Universelle. The *Class M* was series produced, and distributed by the North American Phonograph Co., which passed under Edison's control when it encountered difficulties.

superseding the phonographs so beloved of collectors today, and from 1 October 1913 until production ceased, no Edison machine was made with an external horn.

An important stage in the history of Edison phonographs was the introduction of flat records. There is a similarity of cabinetwork between the *Amberolas* and the *Disc Phonographs*. Although he had been reluctant to change his method of recording (he remained faithful to the 'hill and dale' system) Thomas A. Edison succeeded in making excellent discs, for playing on phonographs giving very good reproduction. Special demonstration concerts were organised at which singers performed the same works both vocally and on record, to convince audiences that there was no difference between the two. The war boom of 1914-1918 was very much to Edison's advantage, as the U.S. army ordered phonographs in quantity to entertain the troops.

For the sake of completeness this chapter on the famous American industrialist must make mention of the miniature phonograph which he built into the body of a doll in 1889; he quickly abandoned production, however, in view of the poor results. Nonetheless, Edison's interest in talking machines lasted for a very long time. He first became interested at the age of 30, and did not give up until he was 82. Two years later he died, having always had a soft spot for this invention, despite the fact that he was deaf.

The Edison *Home Phonograph* was manufactured from 1896 until 1901. It was a solid, spring-driven machine sold for home listening for 40 dollars, and used the Edison wax cylinders, recorded acoustically.

Above right: The most widely sold of the Edison machines was the *Standard*. It was normally sold with a short horn, but the model shown here has been fitted with a long brass horn suspended from a gibbet, giving the machine a rather unusual air.

Opposite page, left: Practically all Edison phonographs could be adapted to use the Bettini 'spider' diaphragm, which gave the machine better reproduction. Here an Edison *Gem* has been fitted with the Bettini system.

Opposite page, right: The Edison *Gem* was the bottom-of-the-list phonograph, which was sold for 7.50 dollars. Although at the price it sold well, sound reproduction was far from satisfactory, the motor being very noisy. Shown is the Model A (1901-1905).

Left and above: The Edison *Concert* phonograph was brought out in response to the demand for louder wax-cylinder reproduction. This model was made between 1899 and 1901. It sold for the high price of 125 dollars. It was provided with a strong, triple spring motor, which enabled it to play six to eight Stentor cylinders without being rewound.

Below: In 1897, Edison brought out his *Standard Phonograph Model A*, which originally sold for 20 dollars. The second version, shown here, came out after 1900. The machine played *Standard* cylinders only, which had a playing time of two minutes. With this machine, Edison became the leader in the phonograph market.

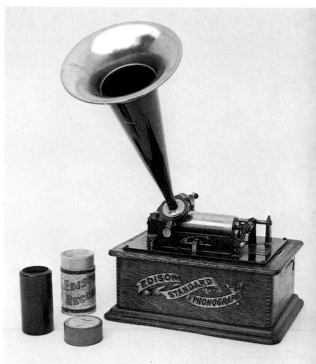

Another version of the Edison *Home Phonograph* with a swan-neck floral horn. The machine could play both two- and four-minute cylinders, and is fitted with the *Diamond Model B* diaphragm.

A superior version of the *Home Phonograph*, the Edison *Triumph* gave an excellent performance for its time. The machine here is fitted for two- and four-minute cylinders, and has the O diaphragm. A simple turn of its lever placed the sapphire needle in contact with the cylinder. Several cylinders could be played without rewinding.

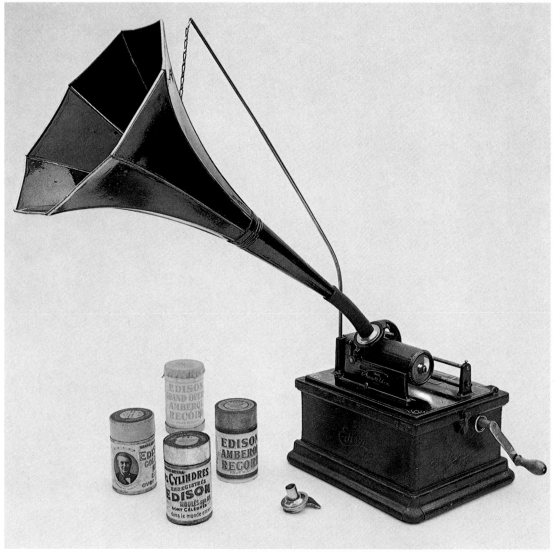

One of the last Edison phonographs to have an ▶ exterior horn, the *Opera Phonograph* came out in 1911 and was sold for only two years. It featured a new system whereby the cylinders moved under the needle rather than vice-versa. A *Diamond A* diaphragm was fitted. The horn is made of mahogany, and rests on a solid support.

Left: The *Fireside* was launched in 1909, at the same time as the four-minute cylinder. The phonograph was adapted to take both two- and four-minute cylinders. The Model *A*, shown here, had an octagonal floral horn.

Edison *Diamond* disc records contin- ▶ ued to use the 'hill-and-dale' record-ing as used on the cylinders, and the grooves were very narrow, so that they could only be played on an Edison machine. The *London 35* gramophone shown here had a special diaphragm which was directly connected to the internal horn, and moved along the grooves of the disc.

Far right: A very rare model, which ▶▶ was specially made during the First World War to entertain American troops in the field. The playing arm took various diaphragms adapted to different sorts of records. The manu-facturer's label carried the letters A and N for Army and Navy, and the case was made extra strong to protect the mechanism in transit.

An advertisement for Bettini phonographs that appeared in 1902 in *Femina*. The panel on the right drew attention to the famous artists who recorded for the enterprising Lieutenant. Note also the high prices demanded for his luxury machines.

In this announcement of 1902/3, Bettini drew attention to all the possibilities of the phonograph. He pointed out that in every circle, it could awake the strongest and most agreeable sensations, it could instruct, distract, and banish solitude. It could awaken the past, and bring the absent nearer, carrying its message to all parts of the world and preserving it for posterity. For parties, it alone furnished a whole budget of entertainment, while for the sick and for children it was the pastime par excellence... Special rebate for soldiers!

BETTINI

Here, without doubt, we have the most picturesque character in the early history of phonographs. Born at Novara in Piedmont in 1860, Gianni Bettini first of all read Classics, then entered the army and was quickly promoted to lieutenant. Very dashing, no doubt, in his cavalry uniform, the young Italian cut quite a swath in society. Attracted perhaps by his moustaches, an American girl named Daisy Abbot took up with him when they met in Paris. Bettini was 25 and in love. He resigned from the army and the pair embarked for the United States, where they eventually married. It is not known what work, if any, Bettini did after his marriage; he had plenty of time to spare, his in-laws being well-to-do, and he became interested in a new invention, the phonograph, which by 1888 had already begun to catch on. The machine he bought was one of the new wax-cylinder Edisons, designed really for dictating letters, and for recording and reproducing speech. An opera lover, like all Italians, Bettini wished, naturally, to record operatic airs. He found the results disappointing. He decided to experiment and this is where Bettini's contribution begins.

He turned first of all to the sound-box. The stylus in an Edison was attached to the diaphragm at the central point. Why not multiply the points of attachment, arranging them symmetrically about the centre? Bettini therefore designed a sort of spider to carry the sapphire with legs of equal length to spread the sound vibrations over the entire diaphragm. Once having got his micro-reproducer to work, Lieutenant Bettini had only one idea: to record the most famous voices. America was not short of these in the 1890's and Bettini had hosts of musical friends. He opened a recording studio at 110 Fifth Avenue, New York, and set to work. Among the voices he captured were those — to take some at random — of Emilio de Gorgorza, Dante del Papa, Mario Ancona and Frances Saville. His records and sound-boxes brought Bettini some measure of fame, despite the small output of his factory.

In an 1896 issue of *The Phonoscope* magazine there is a description of his Fifth Avenue premises and the phonograms recorded. The writer praises the quality of reproduction, and mentions also some cylinders cut by Yvette Guilbert in New York.

As may be imagined, Bettini built up a fantastic collection of celebrity cylinders. As improved copying methods came in, Bettini was able to offer, by 1897, an imposing and splendid list. He also patented certain ideas concerning phonograph manufacture, although he made no attempt to exploit these patents in the U.S., reasoning, no doubt, that vested interests were too strong. In 1898

Bettini in 1914, with the cinema projector he invented. Celluloid film was replaced by a glass plate on which the images were grouped in thirty-six rows of sixteen views. His system, much cheaper than ordinary film, was not developed, and Bettini did not make his fortune with it.

he started a French company, *Phonographes Bettini*, at 23 Boulevard des Capucines, Paris, made over the patents to them and personally took charge. Bettini's efforts were rewarded by a Gold Medal at the great Exposition Universelle in Paris in 1900. Here is the range of instruments offered by Bettini in November, 1901:

Le Numéro 6	50 francs
Le Rubis	56 francs
Le Tandem (for two cylinders)	190 francs
Le Brillant (de-luxe model)	280 francs
L'Aiglon (de-luxe model with four cylinders)	380 francs

Recordings of Hungarian gipsy music, very fashionable at that time, were offered. The quality of the instruments and recordings is unquestionable, but production must have been on a fairly small scale for examples today are very hard to find.

Because legend seems to surround Lieutenant Gianni Bettini, mention must be made of the most legendary episode of all. This took place in 1903 when he recorded the voice of Giocchino Pecci, born 1810 and better known to history as Pope Leo XIII. Here is Bettini's own account of it, as given to an Italian reporter: 'From the moment of entering the Vatican I tried hard not to get over excited. This was a very very delicate assignment, which could so easily go wrong...

'Suddenly the door opened and the Holy Father appeared, clad in white, a majestic figure upon whom the weight of years sat very lightly. He moved with short quick steps towards the Papal throne and took his seat. «So, Mr Bettini, you have come to carry out an experiment. I understand that you have made some remarkable discoveries.» Then His Holiness added: «Now tell me, Bettini, would you prefer me to be, seated or standing up?» I should have preferred, for the sake of the recording, for His Holiness to remain standing, but I did not wish to tire the venerable pontiff and begged him to remain seated. A table was brought and placed as close as possible to the throne, and immediately the Pope intoned the Benediction in Latin. The moment the machine stopped, His Holiness, showing a lively interest in this scientific miracle, requested to hear what he had spoken. Alas, the sound-box had not rendered the words very distinctly, and the Pope did not seem satisfied. But when, after reciting the Ave Maria, His Holiness heard his voice ring out clear and vibrant from the machine, he expressed his satisfaction in the warmest tones, exclaiming: «Good, very good! And now let us have the Benediction again.» I set the machine going and this time, as we know, with complete success.'

A few months later Pope Leo XIII died, in his 94th year. The remarkable Papal record was released by Bettini, and later re-issued by the COLUMBIA GRAPHOPHONE COMPANY. It represents one of the few occasions when such a record was made by the personnage concerned; speeches by the French President or the Tsar of Russia were usually spoken by an actor — possibly Pathé himself.

Bettini's recording diaphragm type *R*, New York patents of August 1889 and December 1892, showing the 'spider' and the mica insets.

Phonograph sold by the Société des Micro-Phonographes Bettini, Paris. The counter-weighted
Model *N* diaphragm was protected by New York patents in August 1889 and December 1892.

Lieutenant Bettini in his studio in New York, shown with one of his *Micro-Phonographs*.

The divine Sarah Bernhardt making a recording for Bettini in his Fifth Avenue studio. It is interesting to note that the engraving was obviously made from a photograph of the actual studio, as shown above.

So Lieutenant Bettini lived up to his legend. Despite his small output, he has an important place in the history of the phonograph. The fabulous collection of recordings he produced was brought back to Europe and destroyed, apparently, in the First World War. Collectors hunt eagerly for any remains.

In about 1905 Bettini changed to flat records and built a small number of disc playing machines. Little is known of this aspect of the firm's production.

Phonographs were not by any means Bettini's only interest. He invented a cigarette lighter and an improved acetylene lamp, and also a slot machine for selling sweets; he also dreamed up a system of cinematography using mobile glass plates which aroused interest at the time but never reached the market. In 1914 Bettini became a war correspondent, covering the Western Front for *Le Gaulois*; in 1917 he was sent back to the United States by the Italian government as part of a military mission. He died in 1938.

Bettini is known to have experimented with the disc gramophone, but whether any were actually commercialized is not certain. It is interesting, therefore, to study the Bettini No. 22, shown here incomplete, which was covered by patent No. 334449 of 6 August 1903.

The Edison stand at the Paris Exposition Universelle of 1889. Only a portion of the phonograph can be seen, but the spider's web of rubber tubes leading to individual earphones gives an idea of the number of people who could listen to a single cylinder.

70

The Phonograph in Europe

Luckily, the child is well-behaved, for its nurse seems to be completely absorbed in listening to the Edison phonograph.

THE UNIVERSAL EXHIBITION OF 1889

The idea of holding a great Paris Exhibition to coincide with Centenary celebrations of the French Revolution was a brilliant one, guaranteeing a maximum of publicity throughout the world. Gustav Eiffel's soaring tower symbolised progress and technology on the grand scale; nations vied with one another to be represented. Paris was the leader of fashion, the Exposition Universelle, a springboard for all those enterprising enough to take part.

The young American firms who had looked to the Paris exhibition to establish the reputation of their talking machines were by no means disappointed. Between 6 May and 6 November the show was thronged by 25 million visitors. Monsieur Sadi Carnot, President of the Republic, had ample cause for satisfaction, for the exhibition had been largely financed by government money.

Thomas Alva Edison crossed the Atlantic with samples of all his inventions. His stands occupied 7,270 square feet, one part being devoted to electric lighting, others to the phonograph and the telephone. The public queued eagerly at the listening booths. The phonographs stood on tables, with an attendant to change the cylinders, and rubber tubes with earpieces led to listening booths around each table. People awaiting their turn looked in astonishment at listener's faces, unable to explain the rapt expressions and sudden outbursts of mirth.

Apparently no phonographs were on sale during the Exhibition, but Edison was planning his publicity campaign. On 23 April, shortly before the opening, a

71

'new' Edison phonograph was shown to the Académie des Sciences in Paris. Speaking on that occasion Edison's man, Colonel Gouraud, told them:

'One of your most eminent composers, Monsieur Gounod, when he heard himself sing his *Ave Maria* to his *own* accompaniment, exclaimed: «How glad I am I made no mistakes! How true to life, but how forgiving». And how is it done? By a few bits of wood, some tin and some wax — simplicity itself, like all great inventions... and of course, by the genius of Edison himself.'

This Académie presentation, eleven years after the first, showed clearly how things had progressed. Tin foil had given way to wax-coated cardboard cylinders, much to the benefit of sound reproduction. The great interest now aroused was to gather momentum during this exhibition year of 1889.

During the exhibition, Edison expressed a wish to meet the man of the moment, Gustave Eiffel. At the resulting interview Edison presented the great man with a phonograph, and this was promptly installed in Eiffel's apartments on the third floor of the Tower.

A second instrument was presented to the Conservatoire National des Arts et Métiers (the Science Museum or Smithsonian Institution of France) where it is still to be seen. Edison is said also to have met Henri Lioret, the clockmaker whose phonographic work is discussed in the next chapter.

Edison did not exhibit his talking dolls. Manufacture of these had started in May, 1889, but the results were unconvincing and he stopped production the following year.

Edison's phonographs in the Machine Gallery were the talk of Paris. Magazines, scientific and otherwise, were full of articles on the American inventor. Meanwhile elsewhere at the exhibition, on another and smaller stand, the *graphophone* of Charles Sumner Tainter played away, while Tainter himself strove to cash in on Edison's fame. Tainter's apparatus had one big advantage: it could be used for dictating letters, and would play them back for the typist. All this worked perfectly, but Tainter's personality and resources were by no means equal to Edison's.

The exposition was widely covered; some of the comments now seem rather naive. One press man wrote that the apparatus 'could pronounce the most difficult diphthongs'. Another said: 'We listened to ballads sung several weeks previously and the voice of the songstress, although stored for a whole month, had lost none of its freshness nor its power to move. This marvellous instrument can speak any language. Prince Taïab-Bey addressed it in Arabic, and Mistral in Provençal: the phonograph repeated their words with every inflexion of the voice and the accent of each speaker.'

Someone proposed forming a 'sort of library in which to lodge phonograms engraved by prominent personages in order to bequeath their voices to posterity'. This has eventually been done, with the creation of the Musée de la Parole, and the BBC Sound Archives. Why did we have to wait so long?

The engraving was published during the 1889 Exposition Universelle, and showed what an attraction the Edison phonograph could be.

Thanks to the enormous trumpet, piano music could be recorded on a wax cylinder.

HENRI LIORET

Henri Lioret in about 1900.

◄ Dolls made by the Maison Jumeau containing phonographs by Henri Lioret. They were brought out for the end of 1893, and featured the first French-made phonograph to play a celluloid cylinder.

On 26 June, 1848 there was rejoicing in the Lioret family. A small Henri was born. His father, a clockmaker at Moret-sur-Loing in the Seine et Marne department, had no doubts concerning the boy's future: as soon as he was old enough he would carry on the family business. Everything went according to plan, and in 1862 Henri Lioret entered the Ecole d'Horlogerie at Besançon. Four years later he left college having completed the course. Henri did well, and founded a business in Paris. His inventive talent led him to design an alarm watch, known as Le Grillon, the Cricket. He won a Bronze Medal at the Paris Exhibition in 1878 and a Diplome d'Honneur in 1879. The government ordered a very grand Lioret clock showing the hours, days, months and seasons. This remarkable piece was presented by the French Republic to the Tsar of Russia.

His career prospered, and at the age of 45 Lioret saw no reason to change; but a chance meeting was soon to turn his life upside down, he was asked to adopt a little girl. She was only 2ft 6in. tall and lacked the power of speech; but she had lovely eyes and a flawless porcelain complexion. Her father's name was Emile Jumeau, and he hoped that her adopted father might be able to make her speak. The miracle was wrought by the end of 1893, and she became known as the *Bébé Phonographe*. Lioret was familiar with the work of Edison and Tainter, and had seen talking machines at the 1889 Exposition Universelle. He also knew of Edison's dolls, and understood why they had failed; their cylinders could not be changed, and the cylinders themselves were too fragile. Thus Lioret built the first French phonograph, which, installed in the Bébé Jumeau became a great success.

Henri Lioret invented a celluloid cylinder, patented on 28 November, 1893 (Supplement to Patent 230177 of 18 May, 1893). These cylinders were immersed in camphorated alcohol prior to recording so that the engraving would take. The new material gave good results and lasted well. The talking *Bébé* was given a good choice of speeches and songs, the doll itself was pretty; and parents willingly stumped up 38 francs, the price of a *Bébé Jumeau phonographe*. Lioret opened large workshops at 18 rue Thibaud in the *XIV arrondissement* and set about increasing production and widening his range. One of these talking dolls he called, with tongue in cheek I fancy, *Le Merveilleux*. Cashing in on the craze, Lioret suggested phonographic advertisements. His best known client was Chocolat Menier, who housed the mechanism to speak their slogan in a charming minature Morris column. These early players were known as *Lioretgraph No. 1*, spelt *à l'américaine*, with no *e* at the end.

Lioretgraph No. 2 reflected the high-class clockmaking which Henri Lioret had practised for so long. This phonograph was developed during the years 1895, 1896 and 1897. Its first selling point was price, much lower than that of the latest American machines; the second that, thanks to its 'resonator', the instrument spoke 'out loud' — although tubes for use with an earpiece were also supplied. The cylinders were made of celluloid; they had a duration of two minutes, but were shorter than American wax cylinders because the grooves, being finer, could be closer together.

Pursuing this idea of 'loudspeaker' phonographs, Lioret built a special instrument and gave demonstrations in theatres and concert halls. In 1897 he leased the old Trocadéro for hearings of *Lioretgraph No. 3*, which was fitted with two horns, one an extension of the other. Despite the bad acoustics at the Trocadéro the demonstration succeeded. It really looks as though Henri Lioret already saw these 'loudspeakers' as a substitute for live concerts, opera and vaudeville. This was premature, of course, and there proved to be little immediate future for the publicity applications. Output from the Lioret works in the Rue Thibaud was never large, although the quality was high.

Feeling overwhelmed by the volume production of the large American companies, Lioret decided, in about 1900, to widen his range by modifying EDISON and COLUMBIA machines. He added a heavy flywheel governor, and substituted his own horn.

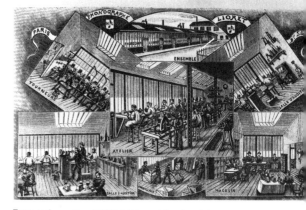

Extract from the 1900 Maison Lioret catalogue.

Caricature of Lioret the clockmaker, about 1890.

Storing cylinders was always a problem, even for the less fragile Lioret celluloid cylinders. This protective box, sold by Henri Lioret, was doubtless a welcome solution to the problem.

76

A sheet metal Morris column 48 cm (18.8 ins) high, printed with advertisements for Menier chocolate. The phonograph concealed inside also puffed Menier's wares (1895).

By modifying the mandrel he enabled both wax and celluloid cylinders to be used. The 1900 catalogue of the Maison Lioret lists the whole range of machines manufactured or modified.

When flat records superseded the cylinder, Henri Lioret manufactured his own, adopting the hill-and-dale system; here he was overtaken by large-scale competition from PATHÉ BROTHERS (founded in 1906).

During his ten years involvement with phonographs, Lioret also built many automata: a clown who drew pictures, a Pierrot, and a soldier boy blowing his bugle. In each case the 'voice' was a Lioretgraph and appropriate cylinder. By the door of the auditorium Lioret had built at the Rue Thibaud, a footman welcomed visitors with a few well chosen words; he was of course a life-size automaton designed by Henri Lioret.

In his use of such modern publicity Lioret showed himself to have been no ordinary man. He was 45 when he first took up phonographs. He organised press publicity, he held numerous demonstrations. Besides his own auditorium and the Trocadéro, he had a small shop in the fashionable Avenue de l'Opéra, and fitted it up for auditions. During the Paris Exposition Universelle of 1900 Lioret did as Edison had done 11 years before, putting on public auditions outside and charging admission. These made him a lot of money — even at 10 centimes a head.

Henri Lioret remained a craftsman all his life, delighting in experiment and making things with his hands. He continued to invent things long after his phonograph days, in both phonetics and motion pictures. This led to collaboration with Léon Gaumont, Fernand Ducretet, the Abbé Rousselot and others. When in 1925, a serious operation obliged him to lead a more sedentary life, Henri Lioret discovered yet another interest, painting. Landscape especially appealed to him, and he made many studies of Moret-sur-Loing, the town where he was born. Lioret lived to be 90, and died in Paris on 19 May, 1938.

The *Lioretgraph No. 1* was presented in a cardboard box under the name of *Merveilleux*. The machine took No. 1 cylinders with a playing time of thirty seconds.

Instructions for the fixing of the metal horn and praising the improvement in the resonator, dating from 1897.

Right: An engraving showing the demonstration of the weight-driven *Lioretgraph* in the Paris Trocadero, 1897. ▶

Phonographe Système Lioret Bte S. G. D. G. Patent

LE PHONOGRAPHE LIORET
DE FABRICATION
EXCLUSIVEMENT FRANÇAISE
Parle et chante aussi haut et aussi distinctement que la voix humaine.

Ne pas Confondre
Avec les Appareils similaires dits
" HAUTS PARLEURS "

AVIS IMPORTANT

Nous avons apporté un nouveau perfectionnement à nos appareils à GRAND PAVILLON.

L'objet de ce perfectionnement est une masse métallique qui, placée à l'intérieur du pavillon et fixée à ce dernier par un écrou extérieur, lui donne une grande stabilité, tout en le laissant très libre dans ses mouvements, et par suite, évite les vibrations que pourraient produire des sons très intenses.

— Pour éviter tout accident nous livrons à part cet accessoire; pour le mettre en place, il suffit de placer la masse à l'intérieur du pavillon, de faire passer la tige filetée par l'ouverture pratiquée à cet effet, de placer la rondelle, le caoutchouc contre le pavillon, et de visser l'écrou.

Nous conseillons à nos clients de séparer la masse du pavillon chaque fois qu'ils ont à transporter l'appareil.

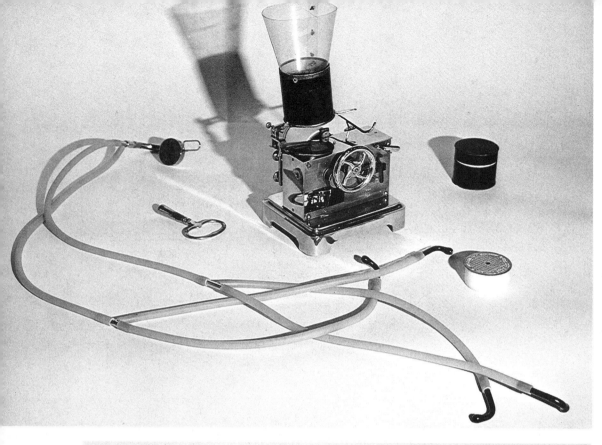

The *Lioretgraph No. 2* with the special diaphragm for use with earphones. The multiple-membrane resonator was also supplied with the machine. Above: Detail of the cylinder and mounting.

Left: A *Lioretgraph No. 2* in its box with the accessories and instructions for use. Below: The machine set up for playing. It was sold by a firm rejoicing in the appellation 'House of New and Practical Inventions' of Paris, who christened the device the 'Salon Phonograph'.

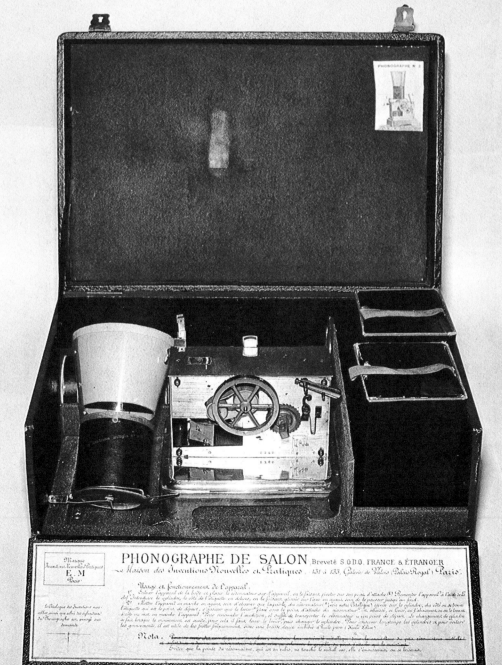

Lioret's improvements consisted of a horn furnished with a large metal diaphragm, a larger regulating wheel, and the replacement of the butterfly regulator by a ball governor.

The *Lioretgraph No. 2* carries the small regulating wheel and the butterfly regulator. It is the first version of the machine with the 1898 improvements.

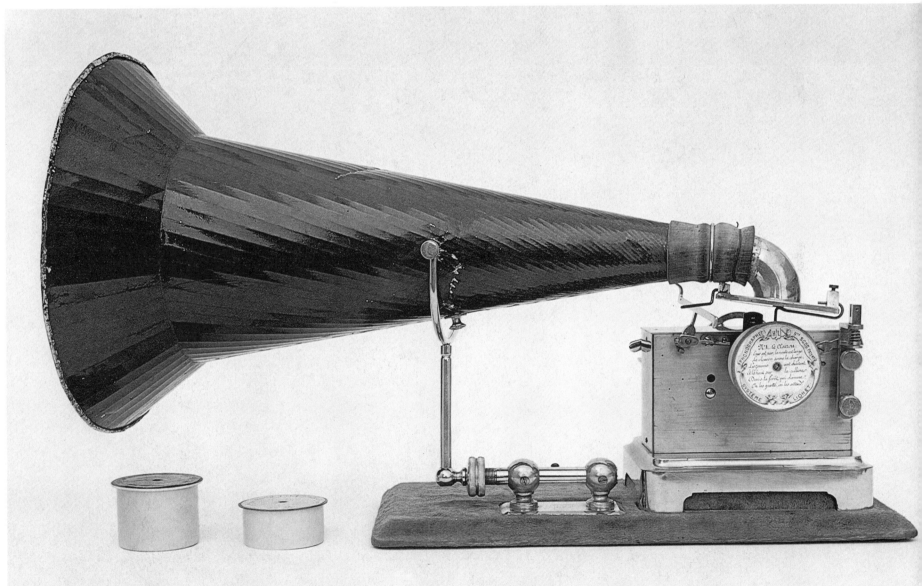

An extract from the 1900 Lioret catalogue, advertising the weight-driven *Lioretgraph No. 3* and its
four-minute cylinders.

Left and right: The weight-driven *Lioretgraph
No. 3*, capable of playing the No. 4 cylinders
which had four minutes playing time. The horn
was of aluminium, the weights in cast iron. It was
possible to conceal the collapsible tripod legs by
a silk curtain attached to the small pelmet that
surrounded the base.

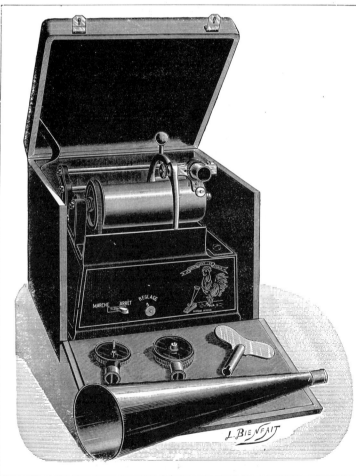

THE PATHÉ BROTHERS

Emile Pathé, head of the photographic branch of Pathé Frères from 1896.

The importance of the Pathé Brothers, who played such a prominent part in the development of both cylinder and disc instruments in France, is such that they deserve a chapter to themselves. It is interesting to follow the development of this firm from the first years of the century, and to observe the impetus that can be imparted to such a concern by one able, determined — and self-made man.

Charles Pathé was born in 1863. He left school at 14 and immediately went out to work; then, although by no means robust, managed his five years military service, which ended in 1888. Next, feeling that a period overseas might improve his social position, he betook himself to South America; but he could not find a good job and the climate did not suit him. In 1891 he returned to Paris, going to work for a lawyer in the Rue de Rivoli, but this was not what he wanted, of course: his one ambition was to start his own small business.

Then one day in August 1894, strolling through the fair at Vincennes, he stood fascinated by one of the sideshows: an Edison phonograph. No doubt if Pathé had been in Paris for the 1889 Exposition Universelle the idea of exploiting this gadget would have occurred to him sooner. By brisk mental arithmetic Charles saw that each two-minute performance brought in 1.50 to 2 francs, one phonograph being connected to twenty or so auditors. Straight away he threw up his job and set about raising the necessary capital: 1,000 francs for an Edison phonograph plus 800 francs for cylinders, batteries and so on. Within a few days Charles Pathé had his machine and knew how to use it. On 9 September, 1894 he made for a fair on the outskirts of Paris and set up his booth. That first day brought in 200 francs. Thereafter he worked the fairs and other places of pilgrimage. Crowds meant money. The fairground folk were amazed at the sums Pathé raked in, so he sold them phonographs of their own. Soon Pathé was buying Edisons wholesale and importing them from E.O. Kumberg in London. Charles Pathé was launched on his commercial career.

In order to keep his customers to himself, Pathé decided to supply them with cylinders pressed by himself at his little place in the Cours de Vincennes. Famous opera singers and vaudeville artistes beat a path to his door; but as Pathé later confessed in his memoirs, it was he and not President Sadi Carnot who spoke the rousing words of the Lyons speech into the recording-horn. The Pathé firm's first commercial address was 72, Cours de Vincennes, Paris, but these premises were merely the humble beginning.

The original PATHÉ FRÈRES company dated from 1896 when Charles Pathé

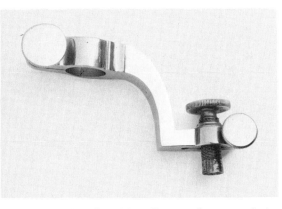

A plane for wiping off a recording on a cylinder to be re-used.

◀ Left: A Pathé Frères advertisement for their *Gaulois* phonograph.

was joined by his brother Emile, and cinematography was added to the firm's activities. There were henceforth two branches to the firm: Talking Machines and Cinematography.

Soon considerable expansion was made possible by new capital brought in by a M. Crivolas which led to the founding in December 1897 of the COMPAGNIE GÉNÉRALE DES CINÉMATOGRAPHES, PHONOGRAPHES ET PELLICULES, with registered offices at 98, rue de Richelieu in Paris. These premises were exactly opposite the Werner company, importers of phonographs from America.

The Pathé brothers' company did not manufacture phonographs. At first they marketed American products: GRAPHOPHONE in the lower price range and EDISON for those willing to pay more. Soon the recording and publishing sides assumed a greater importance, and Pathé marketed machines. Sailing rather close to the wind, the ex-Maison Pathé had the *Graphophone Eagle* copied and called it *Le Coq* — exchanging an American national bird for a French. Actual manufacturers were ETABLISSEMENTS CONTINSONZA, rue des Envierges, Paris, and the MANUFACTURE FRANÇAISE D'APPAREILS DE PRÉCISION, 25-27, boulevard de Belleville, Paris, as well as the MAISON JAPY of Beaucourt.

Always based closely on American models, the first Pathé phonographs showed little originality, but gradually French taste won through. '*Je chante haut et clair*' sounded well as a slogan, and a fine range of fancy horns was available in various shapes and materials. Among those in the 1899 catalogue we find sheet-metal, cardboard, nickel-plated brass, aluminium, and tinplate; also grander designs in different kinds of glass; plain, lustre or with engraved decoration and gilt.

The remarkable growth in cylinder production led to the acquisition of land at Chatou, just west of Paris on the Seine, for a new factory.

Blank cylinders (for home recording) cost 1 fr 50 each; recorded ones, 3 fr 50. In 1899 these prices fell to 1 fr 25 and 2 fr 50 respectively.

Every month the catalogue contained new attractions. PATHÉ drew upon all the stars in show business: Sarah Bernhardt, Coquelin, Fragson, and other big names. For popular songs, recitations and so on, they had artistes recording all the year round to produce the thousands of cylinders demanded by an insatiable public. Among those who specialised in this work and made a name at it were music-hall comedians Charles and Maréchal, while vocalists included Vaguet, Boyer and Aumonier.

The company's capital, originally 1 million (gold) francs, was increased to 2 million in 1899. When in 1901 it rose to 2,666,600 francs the title became COMPAGNIE GÉNÉRALE DE PHONOGRAPHES, CINÉMATOGRAPHES ET APPAREILS DE PRÉCISION. As the company grew, its range of phonographs was widened, and the importing of American machines was discontinued. Credit sales meanwhile ceased to be a responsibility of the parent company, who granted an exclusive concession to the *Etablissements Girard et Boitte*, 42, rue de l'Echiquier, Paris. Payment by instalments brought about an enormous increase in the sale of phonographs, while cylinder-production soared, especially when moulding became possible and performers no longer had to sing themselves hoarse in front of recording-machines.

The same model fitted with the standard aluminium horn.

◄ Previous page, left: The *Pathé No. 1* could play both standard and large diameter cylinders, thanks to exchangeable mandrels. Various versions of the *Pathé No. 1* were available. Its debt to the *Graphophone* is obvious.

Previous page, right: The *Pathé No. 2* of 1904. The motor could play two cylinders without rewinding. It was sold at 75 francs, while the No. 4 cost 175 francs.

In the course of its rapid growth the COMPAGNIE GÉNÉRALE DE PHONOGRAPHES broke free from American machines and transatlantic influences: it became more and more French. GRAPHOPHONE aluminium soundboxes gave way to French imitations marked *P.F.* (Pathé Frères). Next there appeared black ebonite diaphragms. Several types were offered:

Coq	40 mm diameter	*Rex*	55 mm diameter
Coq	45 mm diameter	*Coq*	recording model.

The GRAPHOPHONE machines and their adaptations marketed as *Aiglon, Coq, Gaulois, Stentor, Céleste, Français* and *Coquet*, were replaced by a range known as the *Nouveau Phonographe Pathé*, and numbered as follows:

Model 0	22 fr 50
Model 1	58 fr (with domed lid or reversible box)
Model 2	75 fr
Model 3	130 fr
Model 4	175 fr

Right: Another version of the *Pathé No. 1*. Dating from 1903, it could use the *Vérité* system. The horn, in the shape of a French horn, was made of nickled brass.

◄ Previous page, left: The *Pathé No. 3* was a much bigger machine, capable of playing four or five cylinders without rewinding, thanks to a more powerful motor than those fitted to the lower numbers. Of all the series from No. O to No. 4, it was the first to be discontinued, in about 1905. Previous page, right: The *Royal* was not included in the numbered Pathé models. It was particularly carefully made, but was not sold for long.

All these would play Standard ('*ordinaire*') cylinders and the 9.5 cm (3 ¾ in.) 'Inter' cylinders, which were a Pathé design. The Model 4 *Phonographe* played also the big *Stentor* cylinders. At Chatou special buildings were set aside for the production of these models.

In the spring of 1903 a modification came out enabling several sizes of cylinder to be played. Other great claims were made for this *système Vérité*, which Pathé hailed as a phonographic revolution, 'completely eliminating the nasal tone in all types of instruments'. The *Vérité* suspension system was rather complicated; it was supposed to leave the soundbox free to follow the grooves without undue constraint. Today it is not easy to find instruments with this device intact, though the *Vérité* soundbox was available on all models.

The hundreds of thousands of cylinders recorded since Pathé began had earned not a sou for the authors and composers concerned. In France the SOCIÉTÉ DES AUTEURS, COMPOSITEURS, EDITEURS DE MUSIQUE (S.A.C.E.M.) filed suit against PATHÉ FRÈRES. The case was long and drawn out and eventually decided in favour of S.A.C.E.M. The Society was awarded 500,000 francs damages and interest, and it was held that henceforth a royalty would be payable on every work recorded.

In 1906 Pathé decided to bring out flat disc records in the vertically engraved 'hill and dale' system, and gramophones upon which to play them. By means of a pantograph device (the principal component of which was called a 'fish' on account of its shape) it was possible to engrave discs direct by following the grooves on a cylinder matrix. This process was used by Pathé until they abandoned 'hill and dale'. Master recordings were made on the big *Paradis* cylinders (which could be played on a *Céleste* phonograph) and from these transferred to disc.

The first PATHÉ disc phonograph came out in 1906. It was called *Model A*, and was followed by *Model B*... and so on. Some years later machines were renamed *Pathéphone* and each model given a number. We are talking here of models with external horn. Usually *Pathé-Salon* and *Pathé-Concert* models had the horn built in to the cabinet, as did the *Pathé-Jeunesse*.

Pathé sapphire-played records are generally double-sided, except those made in 1906. Several diameters were made: 21, 24, 29, 35, 40, and 50 centimeters. Records on which the title is engraved play 'backwards', i.e. starting from the centre; records with paper labels play in the normal way.

In the early days of sapphire-stylus records the MAISON PATHÉ brought out two rather unusual machines: *Pathépost* and *Ronéophone*. The former was for recording short messages to be sent through the post, the latter was an office appliance. In the *Pathépost* there were two separate soundboxes, one to record, the other to play; the idea did not catch on. The *Ronéophone*, as its name suggests, was a joint effort by Pathé and Ronéo, makers of office equipment; it was in fact a dictating machine equipped with a large wax disc. After play-back the message could be effaced by shaving a film of wax from the surface. Two versions were made, one driven by electricity, the other by clockwork.

The year 1912 saw the appearance of a 'Pathé spectacular' — a remarkable device for language-teaching by audio-visual means. While the pupil was listen-

A caricature of Emile and Charles Pathé, each carrying the object that represented his occupation — the gramophone and the cinematograph. The cock, trademark of the company, has not been forgotten.

90

The *Céleste* was the largest of the Pathé phonographs, and was the only model capable of playing the Céleste cylinders which were 21 cm (8.2 in) long and 10.5 cm (4.1 in) internal diameter. About 1900, the first version of the *Céleste* was called the *Graphophone No. 800*, despite the fact that only the motor was imported from the United States. Its price then was 1000 francs. In 1903, a lightened *Céleste* model cost 600 francs. The machine shown here is fitted with the *Vérité* system.

CHATOU. — Sortie de l'Usine Pathé

Workers leaving the Pathé factory at Chatou at the end of the day show the large number of people needed to manufacture phonographs and cylinders.

Left: Pathé's letter-heading contained the two trademarks, the Discobolus and the crowing cock.

Below: A rare model of the *Gaulois*, with a wooden case and ornamental feet.

ing to the record, a paper strip unrolled, illustrating the words encountered, and providing a translation. These machines are pretty to watch.

An unusual feature of certain Pathé phonographs was the device known as a 'diffusor'. This consisted of a diaphragm in the form of a paper cone, a sapphire stylus being mounted at the apex; the system was derived from the famous Lumière pleated-paper diaphragms featured by the COMPAGNIE DU GRAMOPHONE. Some instruments equipped with this diffusor had adjustable wooden flaps, allowing the volume to be controlled.

In 1929 PATHÉ abandoned 'hill and dale' recording and went over to needle-played records. Not long after this the company was absorbed by SOCIÉTÉ PATHÉ MARCONI, which in France collated the interests of GRAMOPHONE, COLUMBIA and PATHÉ.

Right: The Pathé *Gaulois* was advertised as a ▶ family phonograph, costing only 36 francs. The first models came out in 1900, but already by 1903 the name was dropped from the catalogue. It was distributed by Girard et Cie, reaching large sales thanks to monthly credit terms. The machine sold in this way was called the *Minstrel*, and was given a varnished wood case and a glass horn.

92

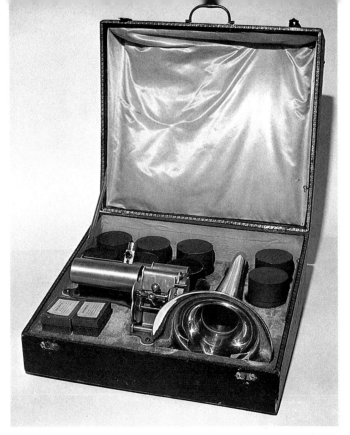

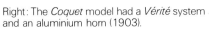

Left: This packaging of the *Graphophone Coq* made by Pathé was called the 'Travelling case'. It contained a No. 25 machine, a Pathé diaphragm, a recording diaphragm, several cylinders and a horn.

Right: The *Coquet* model had a *Vérité* system and an aluminium horn (1903).

Above: *Pathé No. 0*, the simplest of the machines put out by the makers. It was the cheapest also, selling for 22 francs 50. The horn is fixed to a support, and the diaphragm guided by the grooves on the cylinder.

Left: *Model No. 4* was the largest Pathé machine in the 1904 series. It was able to play cylinders of three sizes: standard, intermediate and Stentor, thanks to exchangeable mandrels. It cost 175 francs. As with all the Pathé machines of the time, it could be equipped for recording.

A sentimental postcard showing, *inter alia*, a *Pathé No. D.*

When Pathé brought out hill-and-dale records in 1905, the Model *A*, the simplest gramophone, cost 60 francs.

◄ Left: The 1906 Pathé machines had a remarkable form of sound arm. This is the *Gramophone Model D,* its lid marked with the cock trademark.

Right: The *Pathéphone* with a large floral horn typical of the make. The Discobolus trademark appeared on the front of the case.

Below right: *Pathéphone No. 6* The metal lever seen in front of the case started the turntable, and also stopped the mechanism instantaneously when required.

Below left: The 1908 *Omnibus* gramophone was sold for the popular price of 35 francs. A cheap model, it was nonetheless well-proportioned, but the mechanism was rather weak.

Left: The *Pathé* Model *E* was even more luxurious than the Model *D*. The case was more elaborate, and a speed regulator was fitted to the side next to the winding handle. The aluminium horn shown here is unusual. It had a diameter of 52 cm (20.4 in).

Below and right: The moleskin covered case of this machine is equipped with the first series Pathé sound arm and a metallic blue horn. The effect was obtained by tinning the horn before painting.

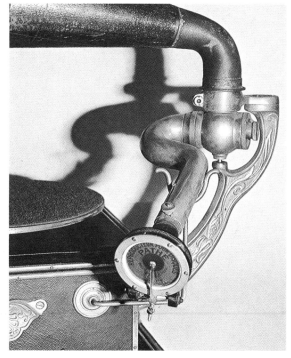

The trademark transfer on a *Pathéphone D*.

Above right: The famous Pathé machine for hill-and-dale records. It was provided with a large cardboard funnel, on the end of which was fixed the sapphire needle. Sound could be regulated by the moveable shutters.

Above left: When the fashion for large external horns started to wane, Pathé made, from 1910-1911, very good gramophones with internal sound boxes. The machine shown here belonged to Jean Noté, the Belgian baritone. It could play 35 cm (14 in) diameter records.

Left: The *Pathé-Jeunesse*, the smallest of the *Salon Pathés*, was made to play records of 21 (8.2 in) and 24 cm (9.4 in) diameter. It cost 25 francs in 1910.

Right: The 1907 model of the Pathé gramophone sold by Girard ▶ et Cie with twenty records for the price of six francs a month for 30 months. It was equipped with a money-box for the provident.

The *Pathé Concert*, a large gramophone for public entertainment operated by a coin in the slot mechanism. The horn is partially concealed by a large moulded-zinc decoration. The turntable was driven by an electric motor, and the gramophone was capable of taking 50 cm (19.6 in) records.

An unusual gramophone from Pathé with twin diaphragms, soundboxes and horns. The distance between the two needles, which followed the same groove, could give rise to an extraordinary echo if they were not carefully synchronized. But sound volume was doubled by the twin sources. One of the diaphragms was reversed in order to play the record from the opposite side.

The *Pathé Diamond* portable, although small, produced a volume of sound that astonished listeners. When the gramophone was folded for carrying, it resembled a camera.

An illustration from the Pathé catalogue for 1899
that seems to have been taken directly from the
other side of the Atlantic!

THE AMERICANS IN EUROPE

Once a phonograph industry had become established in the United States it was essential to find outlets in Europe. This explains the presence of EDISON and COLUMBIA GRAPHOPHONE at all the big international exhibitions from 1889 onwards. The actual importation of talking machines into Europe was no problem; it was another matter to interest Old World listeners in Mr Sousa's marches and American vaudeville sketches. Phonograph manufacturers had therefore to set up recording facilities in each country.

Currency earned from these recordings was not always transferable; so subsidiaries were established in France, Germany, Italy, Britain and elsewhere — although the EDISON BELL PHONOGRAPH COMPANY of London did not quite follow the pattern; for whilst *Gem* and *Standard* models were made in England the *Home* was imported from the U.S.A. By 1910 all EDISON BELL publicity was on a national basis, and the variety of instruments was wide, because by now it included gramophones for flat records and detachable needles.

In France American instruments made an excellent start, but Pathé's reply in the shape of cylinder machines soon outclassed the opposition. The dubious tactics employed by Pathé in copying GRAPHOPHONE and then undercutting, practically extinguished American sales. The advent of hire-purchase further strengthened the French position.

The case of the COMPAGNIE DU GRAMOPHONE was different, as local subsidiaries were established in each important country. Close links were maintained between London and Paris, while the outstanding records obtained by the enterprising and musical Fred Gaisberg in Europe proved remarkably popular in the States, and rapidly reversed the balance of trade.

106

ZONOPHONE

A detail of the motor plate showing the trademark *Zonophone* written in both Roman and Cyrillic characters.

◄ Left: The American *Zonophone No. 2* was distributed in France under that name by the International Zonophone Company. The *Concert V* diaphragm was made by the Universal Talking Machine Manufacturing Co., New York.

The history of the ZONOPHONE COMPANY typifies the struggles in which the early phonograph manufacturers became embroiled. Emile Berliner's colleague, Frank Seaman, foresaw a bright future for disc records with side to side as opposed to hill and dale recording especially in Europe. He lost no time therefore in quitting the GRAMOPHONE COMPANY and setting up on his own. The name ZONOPHONE was chosen (in 1899) because it echoed, more or less, names already established in the American phonograph industry. A representative was immediately dispatched to Europe to explore the marketing possibilities, and it was decided to set up headquarters in Berlin, as competition from the GRAMOPHONE COMPANY would be less fierce there than in London or Paris.

The machines themselves were technically similar to GRAMOPHONES, but outwardly rather different. ZONOPHONE records, too, were imaginatively presented, with differently coloured labels being used for each kind: light music, military bands, and humorous sketches were black or green, while 'celebrity' and classical records had light blue or orange, printed in gold and silver respectively. Famous artists recording for ZONOPHONE included Aïne Acté, Melchissedech, Delmas, Rose Caron, Fugère, Coquelin — and, of course, Enrico Caruso.

Sales were poor, despite offers of easy terms; reproduction left something to be desired, perhaps, but it was no worse than rival makes. Publicity methods were based on those of the GRAMOPHONE Co.: signed testimonials from famous artistes extolling the merits of the 'admirable Zonophone'. Amongst the signatories were Sarah Bernhardt, Edouard de Reszké, Rose Caron, Delmas, the Coquelin brothers and so on, while the accompanying text introduced the Monster Zonophone and its ebonite records 'attaining the supreme limits of

Left: Offered for sale in France in 1903, this *Zonophone* model did not enjoy a great success. It was the only one to be distributed by Girard et Cie, and was sold for 220 francs payable over 22 months. Included in the price were twenty records, featuring, among others, Coquelin the Elder, Sarah Bernhardt, Rose Caron and Delmas.

Right: A postcard that seems to have been based on the His Master's Voice trademark.

Below: The *Zonophone* known in America as the Type *A*. This particular model was sold by E. Caorsi of Genoa, Italy. The 17 cm (6.6 in) turntable had a small spur to retain records of that size. The machinery was visible through two bevelled glass panels in the case.

perfection' in their rendering of the human voice, and proving equally at home with poetry, drama, music and song. Alas, even this could not keep ZONOPHONE afloat — nor even an offer to take back any record that was worn out, broken or simply no longer wanted, and replace it by a new record free of charge plus another at list price... Not the simplest of offers perhaps; and the moment came when the ZONOPHONE company itself went up for sale. This was just what GRAMOPHONE had been waiting for. They purchased the stocks and catalogue too. Some ZONOPHONE records were re-issued in GRAMOPHONE guise; but the 'celebrities' were dropped since they might conflict with the Red Label series GRAMOPHONE had recently brought out.

Zonophone record label for a recording of the 'Fox and the Crow' made by Coquelin the Elder.

Left: A means of telling apart *Zonophones* from *Gramophones* was that the link between the crane and the diaphragm was metal instead of wood. Another was that the interior of the horn was painted red.

Right: A much simpler version of the *Zonophone*, ▶ although still fitted with the same motor as the others of the same make. It seems to have been the last of the series using a rigid support. The small size of the turntable meant that the brake had to work on the edge and not underneath the turntable, as on the larger models.

Below: A poster for *Zonophone* 'pay as you play' sales dating from June 1903.

110

FRENCH MAKES

The cunning French even persuaded dusky potentates to take their oaths of loyalty into a recording phonograph.

◄ The floral-horned *Siren* was sold in Paris by Morel under the name *Au Sou BB de 1855*. The phonograph carries no other trademark, although of German origin. The *Siren* did well on the French market, its colours having been adapted to French tastes.

The French talking machine industry goes back to 1893, as we have seen, thanks to Henri Lioret, followed by the brothers Pathé. There was much lee-way to make up. American competitors had been campaigning on three fronts. The phonograph as they saw it was primarily an office appliance, a shorthand substitute. Slot-machines in public places could also earn valuable revenue, and they saw a future for home recording. These aspects were not neglected in France, but the French saw other, more specific possibilities. As luck would have it, the talking machine's arrival coincided with that of Art Nouveau, the convolvulus curves and elegant tendrils of which contributed so much to the *Belle Epoque*. Phonograph trumpets assumed the colour of flowers. Suspension standards for acoustic horn and tone arm described graceful arabesques. Colour schemes were very much of their period; carving (machine made) decorated box and cabinet.

The contribution of individual manufacturers is often hard to assess. Some took out patents — in which case all is clear; some made minor modifications to machines 'bought out' for re-sale. Others were straight copies of existing models. The model most often copied was the *Graphophone Eagle*.

Confusion often exists between manufacturers and mere retailers. Often the name of the retailer is known, while the identity of actual maker can only (sometimes) be guessed. This is not surprising when one considers the background of the people concerned: clockmakers, mechanics, men from the cycle trade, sewing machine makers, occasionally makers of musical instruments. Some machines were made up of parts drawn from several sources. It is not uncommon to find a Swiss soundbox or motor on French and Belgian machines, especially after 1920. Small firms sometimes managed to branch out, at the time when cylinders were giving way to the disc. Later new makes appeared, specializing in either hill and dale or lateral recording, and sometimes combining the two, which was better. Model names reflect their period: *Le Merveilleux, Le Charmeur, Le Mélodieux, Le Sublime, Le Virtuose, La Cigale, La Voix d'Or, Eureka, Omega, Phono-Opéra, Paris-Phonographe, Le Cahit, Sonor...* A few makers' names come to mind: CHARDIN-MOREL, CALDAGUES, PERRIN, CANNEVEL...

Big firms invented brand names to denote simplified models selling at lower prices. The best example of this, of course, was the *Diamond* from PATHE.

In early days many small makers built machines but no cylinders or records. This was a mistake from the sales point of view; it also deprived them of a source of revenue, income from records often exceeding that derived from selling machines.

Certain manufacturers owed much of their success to sales on the instalment plan. This aspect will be discussed in a later chapter.

Advertisement for La Maison de la Bonne Presse, appearing in *Le Pèlerin* of 16 October 1898.

Left and below: Placed on the market at the end of 1899 by Girard et Cie, the *Omega* possessed the special feature of a vertical ball governor. Advertisements pretended that 5000 had been ordered, but that seemed an over-estimate considering the very short time it was on sale. The diaphragm is a *Gramophone* model, while the machinery was of French construction.

Two models from *Idéal-Phonographe*. One, (above right) with enamelled motor base, dates from 1900; the other (below) from 1902. They were distributed by La Maison de la Bonne Presse, as was the carefully chosen cylinder collection. The *Idéal-Phonographe* was well constructed of polished brass, or nickel-plated, and had a graduated speed regulator; its main feature was a mobile cylinder mandrel for better reproduction, which allowed cylinders of all dimensions to be played by placing them at varying distances from the diaphragm, in this case the high-quality *Cahit*. Below left: Detail of diaphragm; right: Speed regulator.

Le Colibri, a well-made phonograph, featured a diaphragm and horn that followed the grooves, thanks to a moveable bar fixed to an endless screw. The cylinder frame was of black ebony, the motor cog wheels, brass, except in one model in which they were of hard cardboard for quieter playing. The diaphragms were ebony with a small brass weight for balancing the recorder.

G. Dutreih marketed the *Musica*. This phonograph ► played two cylinder sizes (ordinary and intermediate). A novelty was the bracket for holding the diaphragm when not in use.

A *Colibri* in its black case lined with red felt. This machine's horn is of nickeled brass, whereas the other *Colibri* is aluminium. Left: Instructions for using the *Colibri*.

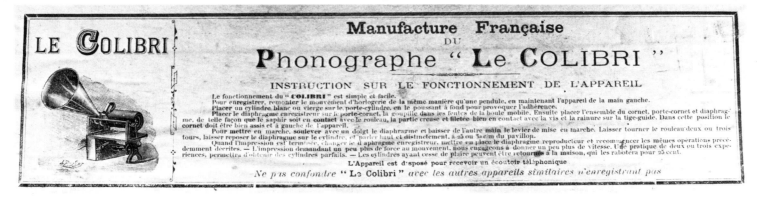

LE COLIBRI

Manufacture Française
DU
Phonographe " Le COLIBRI "

INSTRUCTION SUR LE FONCTIONNEMENT DE L'APPAREIL

Le fonctionnement du " COLIBRI " est simple et facile.
Pour enregistrer, remonter le mouvement d'horlogerie de la même manière qu'une pendule, en maintenant l'appareil de la main gauche.
Placer un cylindre blanc ou vierge sur le porte-cylindre, en le poussant à fond pour provoquer l'adhérence.
Placer le diaphragme enregistreur sur le porte-cornet, la goupille dans les fentes de la boule mobile. Ensuite placer l'ensemble du cornet, porte-cornet et diaphragme, de telle façon que le saphir soit en contact avec le rouleau, la partie creuse et filetée bien en contact avec la vis et la rainure sur la tige-guide. Dans cette position le cornet doit être bien assis et à gauche de l'appareil.
Pour mettre en marche, soulever avec un doigt le diaphragme et baisser de l'autre main le levier de mise en marche. Laisser tourner le rouleau deux ou trois tours, laisser reposer le diaphragme sur le cylindre, et parler haut et distinctement, à 25 ou ¾ cm du pavillon.
Quand l'impression est terminée, changer le diaphragme enregistreur, mettre en place le diaphragme reproducteur et recommencer les mêmes opérations précédemment décrites. — L'impression demandant un peu plus de force au mouvement, nous engageons à donner un peu plus de vitesse. Une pratique de deux ou trois expériences, permettra d'obtenir des cylindres parfaits. — Les cylindres ayant cessé de plaire peuvent être retournés à la maison, qui les rabotera pour 25 cent.

L'Appareil est disposé pour recevoir un écouteur téléphonique

Ne pas confondre " Le Colibri " avec les autres appareils similaires n'enregistrant pas

The *Cannevel,* produced by Le Phonographe Français, was notable not only for its unusually large size. Edouard Cannevel took out several patents for this phonograph and its diaphragm. He and Paul Hébert submitted a patent application on 31 July 1900 for the reproduction of phonograph cylinders by a moulding system after electroplating. Henri Lioret sold the machine under the name *Le Charmeur.*

The cartoon by Robida, which appeared in the *Pêle-Mêle* of 22 October 1899 showed that street singers could profit from the new invention.

The small model *Musica* could also be sold under other trade names, particularly *Au Sou BB de 1855.* The horn was attached to a fixed bar, so that the diaphragm moved in an arc of its radius, to the detriment of reproduction.

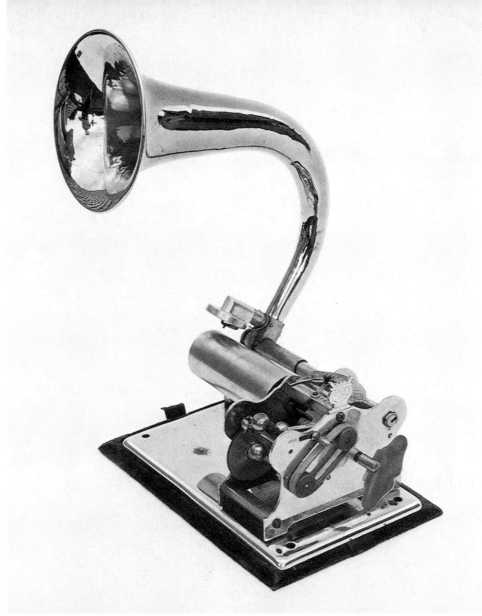

A phonograph made by Charles and Jacques Ullman & Cie, bearing their trademark, a swan in a lyre. Musical instruments specialists, the Ullman brothers were involved in the production of several makes of phonographs and records: *Odéon*, *Phrynis* and *Zonophone*. They had a shop in Paris.

This phonograph, though nameless, has a 7 cm (2.7 in) mandrel, taking *Phenix* cylinders.

La Société des Machines Parlantes A. Combret in Paris produced recording and playing devices, adaptable to any make of phonograph. The large diaphragm reproduction improved the qualities of the machine to which it was fitted. Combret created the *(Sonore) Phono-Opéra* pictured here. In 1906 the firm produced gramophones.

The lyre-shaped phonograph was ► promoted all over Europe. These were invariably produced in Germany, and a small plaque indicating the wholesaler's name was simply added. The floral horn went well with the lyre shape, and the combination was typical of the 1900s.

Below, left and right: This phonograph, sold in France, was made in Germany by G.C. Co. The decoration on the base shows elves playing music.

Sold by La Maison P. Perrin in Paris, the machine was distinguished by a floral horn and a mahogany case, though the actual mechanism was bought in from other makers.

The *Sonor* with four cylinders cost 35.10 francs cash or 39 francs on credit. The lyre-shape phonograph has an unusual horn and a diaphragm of brown ebony, as well as a wooden cylinder mandrel.

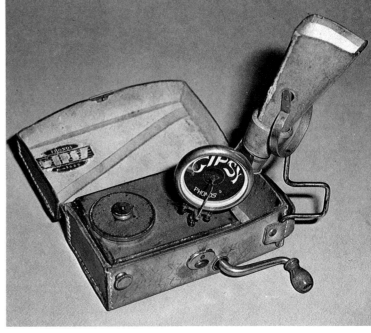

The *Mignonphone* measured only 23 × 12 × 6 cm (9 × 4.7 × 2.3 in) and weighed just 1800 grammes (63 oz). The cardboard horn folded to fit the case.

The *Gipsy* was even smaller, and featured a fine leather case. The diaphragm was Swiss-made. After 1925, Swiss motors and diaphragms were found on many European models.

Chardin, a Parisan precision mechanic, created this unusual lyre shape with a lion's head decoration.

Perfectaphone produced numerous gramophones ▶ and records. The machine here was sold in Paris, although its motor was Swiss-made.

Le *Phono Kid* was presented in 1926 as the very latest marvel of French industry. It could be used with needle or sapphire records (vertical or gramophone recording). Its most remarkable feature was its imitation Chinese lacquer case.

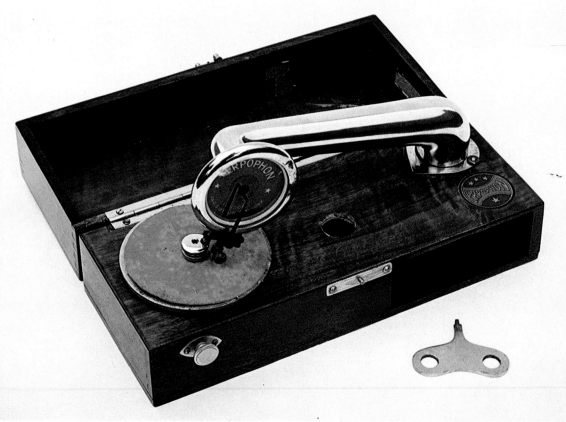

A mahogany-stained *Terpophon*, which was wound up from the bottom. Patents were taken out in London, Paris, Berlin and New York. The model seen in the picture has a curious detail: the transfer reads 'Erpo-phon', the initial T also being painted out on the diaphragm. Perhaps the name had already been registered by another company.

Left: The *American Mélodieux*, which was, despite its name, entirely French. It was distributed by H. Joly of Paris. Another version, which only differed in the size of the cylinder mandrel, was known as *L'Excelsior* and sold by a Libourne firm.

Right: A small floral-horned gramophone that bears no indentifying marks, not even on the diaphragm.

Below: An unidentified gramophone with a mahogany case ornamented with Wedgwood plaques.

GERMAN MACHINES

During the nineteenth century Germany became strongly industrialised. This fact was well known to Thomas A. Edison, who took the precaution of registering his phonograph patents in that country as soon as he had done so in the United States. This did not, however, entail a better sales record than elsewhere for his early tin-foil machines; and the models of 1888/1889 were too expensive for their commercialisation to be easy. The DEUTSCHE EDISON GESELLSCHAFT, established in Cologne, proved rather disappointing. The other U.S. concerns enjoyed varying fortunes. The GRAPHOPHONE COMPANY sold its machines, but as these were of lighter construction than Edison's they were quickly copied by the Germans. The *Graphophone Model Q* was imitated by various firms; the EXCELSIOR and ANGELICA companies produced numerous machines painted in German colours but American in their design.

The GRAMOPHONE COMPANY was more fortunate. Its founder and leading spirit, Emile Berliner, had been born in Hanover; he had preserved his links with the Fatherland and some of his family were still living there. For these reasons he brought over his American inventions. Testing the market with a children's phonograph in about 1889 in association with Kämmerer and Reinhardt, Berliner saw to the launching of the GRAMOPHONE COMPANY in Germany and proceeded to do his native country a considerable service by establishing a formidable pressworks for disc records in Hanover. The registered offices of the DEUTSCHE GRAMMOPHON AKTIENGESELLSCHAFT were in Berlin at Friedrichstrasse 186. This concern was to dominate the German talking machine industry, outselling Zonophone's Berlin operation, which lasted only a few years.

The INTERNATIONAL TALKING MACHINE CO. with its factory at Weissensee, after pressing *Zonophone* discs, went over to pressing for *Odeon*. Also designed at Weissensee, *Odeon Disk* phonographs proved to be a compromise between *Zonophone* and *Gramophone*.

None of these makes showed much originality, as they were all the work of local subsidiaries or mere copies of existing machines. However, there was one field in which Germany was destined to lead the world: talking toys. The German toy industry in 1900 was very large and prosperous; brightly coloured tin trains, boats, cars, tops and so on marked 'Germany' were eagerly imported by Britain and the Continent. The most sought after toy phonographs were the ones which played chocolate records... Manufactured by Unghans, they were

◀ The large *Parlophon* is an excellent example of 1900s style at its most extravagant. The horn support is brass, while the floral horn, 63 cm (24.8 in) in diameter, is painted sheet metal. The case, of painted wood, measures 51 cm (20 in) along each side.

called (1904) STOLLEVERCK in Belgium after a make of chocolate. In France (1903) they sold as EUREKA. There was no advertising sponsorship in the latter country — fortunately for collectors — so some of the records, being of wax and not edible, have survived. Toy phonographs were made in profusion, and although they were pretty flimsy, they played quite well. To sell them, of course, children's records were needed, so each country made records of nursery rhymes and stories. BING, the model train people, made toy phonographs under such names as *Pygmo*, *Gramaphola*, *Gamanette*, and *Nirona* (of which there were several versions).

Amongst cheap cylinder phonographs of simple construction but not made specifically for children, the *Lyre* series may be mentioned. These machines, made from light iron castings, flooded the European market; they needed only a retailer's name-plate to pass as a local product, the national and maker's marks being very discreet.

Sometimes they had the letters GC and C. DEP under the base, and DRGM denoting a German patent. *Lyre* variants are numerous and amusing: Sirens, lions, Lorelei, gnomes, birds and so on. The horn was straight on early models, later floral. The spring motor driving the cylinder-mandrel is like that of a clockwork toy; and because the soundbox is propelled along the cylinder only by the fit of the stylus in the groove, the machine must stand absolutely level. To ensure this a screw foot was provided in the base.

B. Hiller of Berlin devised a phonograph talking clock. Synchronised by a pendulum, the soundbox announced the time from a strip of celluloid marked at intervals with 48 recordings; these represented the quarters, half-hours, three-quarters and hours of the twelve-hour period. Talking clocks came out in 1911 but manufacture was soon discontinued.

The *Klingsor*, from Leipzig, sold well in Britain. Its main feature was a sort of aeolian harp and strings of different lengths stretched across the mouth of the horn. The strings vibrated in sympathy as the music struck them, imparting a special intensity to the sound.

The *Mammut* was, of course, an imposing instrument. It is not uncommon to find coin-operated examples, for its robust construction fitted it well for public use. *Parlophons* were not made in large numbers, but they are notable for their large cabinet and flower-shaped horns.

An unusual small gramophone of German manufacture, stamped with the initials G.C. & Co. for Georges Carette, the famous toymakers. The weight of the diaphragm is compensated for by a spring in the horn support crane, while the turntable is a simple six-spoked wheel. ►

The *Odéon* portable gramophone came with an odd tone arm, curved to fit the metal case. The machine was fitted with the Vadasz system. It dates perhaps from 1925, and is 35 cm (14 in) in diameter.

Above: The *Excelsior* phonograph was made in Cologne, and was derived from the *American Graphophone* Model *Q*. The mandrel was unusual, being made up of three bars. *Excelsior* cylinders were distributed in Germany.

Above left: The *Angelica* was a typical German imitation of the *Graphophone* Model *Q*. However, the painted decorations and the lily-shaped horn gave the machine some originality.

An *Odéon-disk* dating from the beginnings of the make in about 1905. A similarity between certain parts made by the *Zonophone* concern is evident. The diaphragm is marked G.H. No. 15.

The first patents for gramophones equipped with a sort of zither mounted at the mouth of the horn, and which vibrated in sympathy with the sounds coming from it, were taken out in England in 1907. The *Klingsors* were made in Leipzig on the same principle, and the name was chosen to help British sales, since the machine was widely distributed in that country.

A *Klingsor* fitted with a door that concealed the zither. It is a later model than one illustrated above. Manufacture started in 1908 and continued for about fifteen years.

133

'The *Cameraphone* will play any record', was the boast written on the diaphragm of the small folding gramophone marketed in Britain about 1924. The odd shaped sound-box in imitation horn was quite effective.

SUNDRY EUROPEAN MAKES

GREAT BRITAIN   For American phonograph makers the gateway to Europe was England. Edison came first with his tin-foil and later machines: then followed imports by the GRAMOPHONE COMPANY and the GRAPHOPHONE COMPANY. The launching of British subsidiaries led to increased penetration. In 1892 came the EDISON-BELL PHONOGRAPH CORPORATION LIMITED which after various reconstructions built a factory in 1903 at Peckham, London S.E. to make cylinders and certain phonograph models.

In 1898 William Barry Owen, visiting London on behalf of Emile Berliner, founded the GRAMOPHONE COMPANY with offices in Maiden Lane, Strand. In December 1900, this merged with Lamberts, makers of typewriters, to form GRAMOPHONE AND TYPEWRITER LTD. London thus became European headquarters of the GRAMOPHONE COMPANY; discs were made at Hanover and, for the Russian market, Riga. Initially the company's instruments were assembled in England from American parts; then local manufacture was undertaken. As output grew, the works were moved to Hayes, Middlesex, where, later, records were also pressed.

In contrast to the GRAMOPHONE COMPANY, the COLUMBIA PHONOGRAPH COMPANY chose Paris as headquarters in 1897. Three years later, chased away by PATHÉ competition, they moved to London.

Imports of German machines remained very high until the outbreak of the 1914 war, and output from the lesser English makers remained small; but, as we shall see, the importation of soundboxes and motors from Switzerland led to the production of 'novelty' machines such as the *Cameraphone*. When the day of the built-in horn arrived, England made french-polished mahogany cabinets of good quality.

The great Italian make, FONOTIPIA, is noted for a range of fine recordings started towards the end of 1904. With headquarters in Milan, just around the corner, as it were, from La Scala, it was easy to attract the greatest names in Grand Opera. Their catalogue, from 1905 onwards, listed some wonderful talent: Bonci, Maurel, Delmas, Litvinne, Gailhard, Van Dyke, Caron... Only Caruso was lacking, but that great man had an exclusive contract with VICTOR. On 22 April, 1905, the company's special recording machine was taken to Paris, there to make the world's first 14-in. (35 cm diameter) records. The SOCIETA ITALIANA DI FONOTIPIA made the journey to record the famous tenor Jean de Reszké (b. Warsaw 1850, d. Nice 1925). Two sides were made: the tomb scene from Gounod's *Roméo et Juliette*, and Rodrigue's aria 'O Souverain, O juge' from *Le Cid* by Massenet, a rôle which de Reszké had created in 1885. When Jean de Reszké was played these records he insisted that they be destroyed, and never released. Thus ended the saga of FONOTIPIA and Jean de Reszké. From time to time there are rumours that one of the records has turned up, but the rumour is never confirmed, and it is fair to assume that we shall never hear that famous voice. Perhaps it is just as well; distance always lends enchantment, and if de Reszké demanded the destruction of those pressings it may be that he felt he was no longer at the peak of his form...

FONOTIPIA produced a few gramophones, but it was the records which made their name. These continued under the *Odeon* label when FONOTIPIA ceased production. There were close links between these concerns.

Naturally, the big combines also moved into Italy, notably the GRAMOPHONE COMPANY, which made some very fine celebrity records at Milan for their Red Label collection.

The watchmaking skills which made Switzerland leader in the musical-box field led naturally to an interest in phonographs. The town of Sainte-Croix in the Canton Vaud, about 1900, became an important centre for phonograph manufacture: It must be confessed though, that models offered by the THORENS, PAILLARD AND JEANRENAUD firms showed no originality, being the usual rehash of *Graphophone* No. 9 (for cylinders) and *Gramophone* models (for discs). They were well made and reliable, and they were moderately priced. Some models sold well abroad. THORENS made cylinder models under the following names: *Royal*, *Capital*, *Majestic*, and *Minerva*; later came small disc gramophones called *Bijou* and *Helvetia*. After 1910 only the disc models remained, mostly for detachable needles. The 1914 catalogue classed them according to motor-power — 'plays one record', 'plays two records' and so on. The *Sphynx*, *Darling*, *Success*, *Aurora*, *Argentin*, *Concerto*, etc. needed re-winding after one record; *Regalia*, *Organa* and *Orient* played two, *Durban* four, and *Superba*, a long-player, five discs, which seemed to be the maximum.

Numerous Swiss machines were made over the years, one of the last being a portable gramophone in the shape of a camera, which remained in production until the Second World War.

A poster advertising three machines on sale in ▶ Britain about 1903. The *Graphophone* Model *Q* phonograph is shown above, in the centre is a *Gramophone* with a wooden horn support, while *Pathé Graphophone Coq* is shown below, fitted with a *Vérité* support system for the horn and metal sleeve adapters for the mandrel for various sized cylinders.

A curious case in Breton style was supplied with this Thorens gramophone. The *Miraphonic* diaphragm was also made in Sainte-Croix, by Thorens, and was in the best Swiss traditions of precisions work. The case measured 41 x 49 cm (16 x 19.2 in), and was 43 cm (16.9 in) high.

Built by Thorens at Sainte-Croix, the home of the Swiss musical box industry, the *Bijou* was a small gramophone with a painted floral horn. The machine was wound up from above, holes being made in the turntable for this purpose.

Above: The cover of the *Excelda* gramophone has been removed, showing the stowing positions of the tone arm, the diaphragm and the winding handle. The machine dates from 1947.

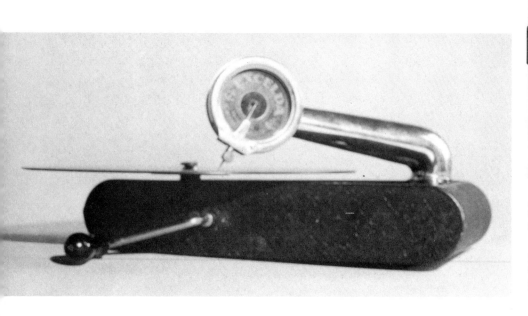

Left: The anchor trademark of the Swiss Thorens concern can be seen clearly on the diaphragm of the *Excelda*. The example shown here dates perhaps from before the Second World War. The closed gramophone resembled a folding camera.

The *Mikiphone* was a folding pocket gramophone, which when closed resembled a Camembert cheese box in metal. An ingenious mechanism allowed all the accessories to be packed into the box, while the black celluloid soundbox was in two parts and could be stored in the case, leaving only the winding handle outside. The turntable was of such small diameter (10 cm — 3.9 in) that records had to be held in place by a central screw.

How many gramophone motors were exported to the rest of Europe is hard to say, but they were certainly fitted to many French and Belgian machines.

The second most important Swiss company was E. PAILLARD, maker of the *Maestrophone*, which carried both a number and a code. This code embraced musicians, compositions, and characters from the opera (from Bach to Mascagni and from *Werther* to *Lakmé*). These mostly had external flower-shaped horns and used detachable needles.

One highly original model was the *Maestrophone No. 205 Polyeucta* which was driven by a hot-air engine, power for which came from a small spirit lamp. Other versions of this model were offered, namely the *206 Benvenuta* and *207 Giordano*. The *208 Lucia* was not a gramophone at all, but a turntable for use in shop window displays.

Another speciality of the Swiss industry were the so-called 'pocket' gramophones, the best known of which was the *Mikiphone*. About the same size when closed as a large Camembert cheese, the Mikiphone unfolded most ingeniously and took 12-in. records. It was described in the Patent as 'Systeme Vadasz'.

The Belgians liked gramophones. They built few themselves (the *Colibri* was one) but they imported a great many.

To Holland, home of his ancestors, Edison accorded preferential treatment. This may explain why examples of Orange, New Jersey design are not uncommon in the Netherlands. The Spaniards enjoyed operatic music. Most leading manufacturers opened branches in Spain.

It was in Russia that the first GRAMOPHONE COMPANY Red Label records were made and the erection by the GRAMOPHONE & TYPEWRITER CO. of a factory at Riga, on the Baltic shows that expectations for the Russian market were high.

OTHER EUROPEAN MAKERS

The early *Phrynis* records had vertical grooving ▶ when they appeared in 1906, but they were soon replaced by lateral groove records under the *Odéon* label. The horn of the *Phrynis No. 10* is unusual in that it has an irregular flower shape.

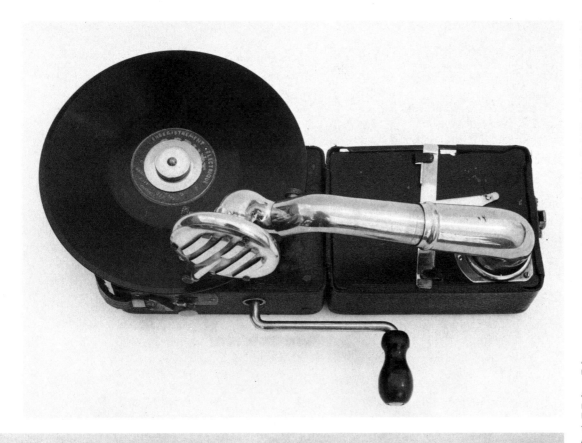

Above: A *Phrynis No. 10* gramophone for needle-played lateral groove records dating from 1909. The machine was made in Switzerland, and seems to have been related to the *Odéon* make. Some diaphragms are marked with a triple U which appears to be the Ullmann trademark, a firm that was connected with the *Odéon* and *Fonotipia* makes, etc.

Left, above and below: The *Colibri*, although marked 'Made in Belgium', had a Swiss-made diaphragm and motor. The model shown here dates from 1930; earlier models having a diaphragm with the mica showing, and carrying the *Colibri* name. It was an expensive machine for its time.

A drawing showing the trio from *Faust* being recorded on cylinders. The singers sing into a trumpet, from which nine tubes lead to nine different cylinders, allowing nine recordings to be made simultaneously. The piano was raised in order to give a better recording.

Promotion and Sales

PERFORMERS RECORDED

As we have seen, manufacturers were at first in two minds. Was the phonograph to be shorthand-writer, or entertainer? The latter prevailed since it involved the entire population.

At first, poor sound quality and the novelty of the whole thing frightened famous performers away. Some time and much persuasion were needed before great stars would venture in front of the recording-trumpet. Generally very great names did not record well. Young performers like Enrico Caruso, on the other hand, adapted magnificently to the new technique. To him and other great singers, talking machines owed much of their early acceptance.

ENRICO CARUSO (1873-1921)

Probably the name of Enrico Caruso would have been famous if gramophones had not been invented; but it is certain that the fame of the little Neapolitan cannot be dissociated from the history of gramophone records.

Born at Naples on 25 February, 1873, Enrico was one of the numerous children of a poor family in that teeming city. Passing rapidly over his comfortless childhood and lack of adequate schooling, we find one consoling feature: music. Enrico sang in a children's choir. He first appeared on the stage in 1894, at the age of 24, without any great success. Gradually young Caruso made a name. He created the tenor rôle in *L'Arlesiana* by Francesco Gilea in 1897, at the Teatro Lirico, Milan, and in Umberto Giordano's *Fedora* a year later, at the

143

same opera house. He then went on tour in Russia and Poland. La Scala, Milan, with no great enthusiasm, witnessed his début there in 1901 in Giacomo Puccini's *La Bohème*. On Friday, 1 February of that year a concert was organised by Arturo Toscanini in memory of Giuseppe Verdi (born 1813) who had died a few days previously at a Milan hotel. The programme included extracts from the Maestro's operas, interpreted by the most famous singers of the day, including Francesco Tamagno, Borgatti, Luppi, Pinto... and Caruso, in the quartette from *Rigoletto*.

Gathering fame with each appearance, Caruso created the rôle in *Germania*, Baron Franchetti's opera, on 11 March, 1902. During a dress rehearsal one member of the audience was especially attentive: Gaisberg of the GRAMOPHONE COMPANY, who had come over to make operatic records and had been told to look out for Caruso.

Gaisberg was convinced. He arranged a recording session for the next week, in a third floor suite at the Grand Hotel, Milan the hotel in which Verdi had died the previous year.

The young tenor, very dapper and stick in hand, arrived after luncheon. The recording phonograph and grand piano (on a temporary platform) were made ready and the accompanist Salvatore Cottone launched into a rousing extract from *Germania*, 'Studenti! Udite!', and Caruso, nervous at first, sang. Gaisberg reassured him; and in less than two hours ten sides had been taken on wax, and Caruso was handed one hundred pounds (£100 sterling) as promised for his part in the performance. The GRAMOPHONE COMPANY directors were horrified at this exorbitant fee, but had agreed. The 'master' records were sent post haste to Hanover to be reproduced, the big factory built by Emile and Joseph Berliner now supplying the whole of Europe. Two months later, while Caruso was singing in London, the Milan recordings were put on sale and widely acclaimed. This timetable seems hardly credible today when records demand an enormous amount of editing and re-recording on tape before they are deemed fit for release.

In fact, this was the first time that the GRAMOPHONE COMPANY technicians had been satisfied with a record. This was due partly, no doubt, to improved materials, but it was due also to Enrico Caruso. His voice, so sensitive and moving, possessed a humanity which came across despite the intervening apparatus: Caruso was at home in all registers; he was, to coin a word, perfectly 'phonogenic'. His was the most successful career on record during the first quarter of the twentieth century.

The Grand Hotel records may not in fact be the first that Caruso made; he did work for other companies about that time. These records are far less well known and even the dates are uncertain. The ANGLO-ITALIAN COMMERCE COMPANY of 6, via Dante, Milan, made some cylinders of Caruso early in 1901. There are three arias:

A young and slim Caruso in the rôle of Torridu in Mascagni's *Cavalleria Rusticana* in 1895: The famous singer was then 22.

> *Tosca 'Recondita armonia'* (Puccini)
> *Les Huguenots 'Sotto il ciel'* (Meyerbeer)
> *'Tu non mi vuoi piu ben'* (A. Pini-Corsi)

144

Enrico Caruso in two rôles which he made famous: the Duke of Mantua in *Rigoletto* and Rudolfo, the poet in *La Bohème*. Caruso left for posterity many recordings of the arias and ensembles of his large repertoire. His recording of 'La donna è mobile' from *Rigoletto* remains a model of bel canto.

A self-caricature by Enrico Caruso recording into a trumpet. His talents as a graphic artist approached those as a singer.

A reciprocal agreement between ANGLO-ITALIAN and the MAISON PATHÉ allowed each company to handle the other's products. Thus PATHÉ released cylinders, and later, sapphire records, of these three arias sung by Caruso. The acoustic quality is good, and the tenor's voice delightful. Why are these early releases so seldom mentioned? Another mystery concerns ZONOPHONE records by Caruso. Were they recorded before or after those made for the GRAMOPHONE CO.? It seems most likely that they were made a few weeks later, perhaps even a matter of days. Indeed, one of these is the aria 'No non chiuder gli occhi vaghi' from *Germania*, created by Caruso on 11 March, 1902. The sound quality on the ZONOPHONE records is not as good technically as on those of the GRAMOPHONE COMPANY. When GRAMOPHONE took over ZONOPHONE the celebrity series (pale blue and orange labels) disappeared and with it the seven sides by Enrico Caruso. Admittedly six of the arias are to be found in both lists; the seventh, 'Un bacio ancora' was never again recorded by Caruso.

GRAMOPHONE COMPANY sales were well organised. The voice of Caruso quickly became known throughout Europe, releases being timed so far as possible with the singer's appearances in each country.

His début at the Metropolitan Opera House, New York, took place on 23 November, 1903, when he sang the Duke of Mantua in *Rigoletto*. It was the first of 607 appearances he was to make in that theatre. In a short while the tenor from Naples was famous throughout the United States. The VICTOR company offered him a contract and on 1 February, 1904, in a New York studio Caruso began his phonographic career in the U.S.A. It did not end until 16 September, 1920, a few months before his death.

Records enable us to follow the evolution of Caruso's voice, as several recording sessions were held every year. Commercially these total 234 sides by Caruso. In addition a certain number were withheld, being considered not good enough for general release. Thanks to pirate editions we have heard some of these, and their defects appear trifling when compared with their inestimable historical value.

Another great success during 1906 was the first operatic duet in the VICTOR classical series. This was 'Solenne in quest'ora' sung by Enrico Caruso (tenor) and Antonio Scotti (baritone). Caruso's voice, despite an increasingly histrionic tendency, retains its 'phonogenic' qualities, and was to retain them indeed until the very end, including the final session at Camden, N.J., in 1920. Even today, despite stereo and the rest, the emotional power of that voice comes through in the re-issues, which continue to sell, year after year.

Caruso amassed a large fortune. This was partly due to his Metropolitan appearances and the worldwide operatic tours; but a great deal came from gramophone records, which between 1902 and his death in 1921, earned him two million dollars. It is amusing to find that Caruso took part in a film — silent of course — an ultimate tribute to the Golden Voice. After 1904 all Caruso recordings were made in the United States, his contract with VICTOR being strict on this point. The immense popularity of Caruso's records has meant that with certain exceptions, they are not rare today.

At the time of his last recording sessions on 14, 15 and 16 September 1920, Caruso was already suffering from the pleuro-pulmonary trouble from which he died less than twelve months later, on 2 August, 1921, in his room at the Vesuvio hotel, in Naples. He had sailed from New York with his young wife and daughter on the liner *President Wilson* on 28 May, 1921, looking forward to a long convalescence in his native land. He rests in the cemetery at Naples, home again after conquering the world with his voice.

Early recordings fall into two main categories: Classical and, for want of a better word, Variety. Generally there was one catalogue of records by little-known (and low paid) artists and another in which famous names figured, to increase the company's prestige. Often 'celebrity' records were sold at a higher price. PATHÉ, for example, offered Paulus *café concert* songs sung by Maréchal, or the great Aristide Bruant's ditties with Charlus or Buffalo singing. The great popularity of the *café-concert* (vaudeville) around 1900 (one thinks of Toulouse-Lautrec) explains the presence of so many comic snaps, sketches and Tyrolean numbers in the catalogues of the period.

The cylinder record provided employment for a whole generation of hack musicians. As there was no way of reproducing a cylinder except by making another recording, durable citizens with lungs of brass were hired to churn out the same number all day long. One of these singers was Charlus.

MUSIC HALL
AND VARIETY

CHARLUS

A recording session at Pathé Frères: Mercadier and Maréchal, two stars of cylinder recordings are shown, one recording while the other reads a score. Taken from *L'Illustration* of 19 August 1899.

Right: Charlus, the jack of all trades of recording, owned to having sung 80,000 times in front of a recording trumpet. He is shown accompanied by a pianist and a clarinetist. The clarinet was an instrument that gave good results on early recordings.

Born in 1860, Charlus began as an imitator of the great café-concert star Paulus — even his name was a crib. He made little headway, competition being strong, and when Emile Pathé asked him to step up and record a few songs nobody could have foreseen the success that his cylinders would have. Charlus rapidly acquired a perfect recording technique. Articulating clearly and keeping his voice within the right compass, he mastered all the tricks of the recording-horn and soundbox diaphragm. Incidentally, every artiste had a soundbox of his own, specially attuned to his voice.

Having sung his way through the repertoires of Paulus and Bruant, Charlus carved a niche for himself, with popular songs, monologues and 'blue' music-hall jokes. He also sang many duets with Madame Bollini, whose speciality was Tyrolean. Every rendering brought Charlus 50 centimes. The coming of moulded cylinders put him practically out of work, despite the 100 fr he was paid for recording each 'master'. However, in 1914, Charlus became area manager for the SOCIÉTÉ PATHÉPHONE at Marseilles, with offices on the Cane-bière. His last recording dates from 1930, for Pathé regarded Charlus as a mascot, whose name would bring luck to their first list of lateral cut needle-played records. Charlus was over 90 when he died.

A much more subtle artiste than Charlus, Yvette Guilbert, born 1867, enjoyed a long and successful career both in France and abroad. Her numbers were witty and considered very daring — especially coming from a woman — but over the years her repertoire widened to include earlier music as well as folk songs and religious works. *Le Fiacre*, Leon Xanrof's place in Paris, put Yvette Guilbert and the long black gloves that were already her trademark, on the map in about 1890. The looks of this lanky *diseuse* are famous thanks to Toulouse-Lautrec, and her career is easy to pinpoint because she left several volumes of memoirs (although oddly enough she does not once mention records). Of these she made a great many, which we shall now discuss.

After a first tour of the United States, in 1894, Yvette Guilbert made a return visit two years later, starting at Koster and Bial's place on 34th Street, New York City. Here she was spotted by the dashing Lieutenant Gianni Bellini who, always on the look-out for talent, invited her to his Fifth Avenue Studio. Six cylinders were recorded: 'I want yer, ma honey' (Templeton), and the same sung in French; 'Petits chagrins' (P. Delmet); 'Par un clair de lune' (P. Marinier); 'Les petits pavés' (P. Delmet); 'La soularde' (J. Jouy).

Her next recordings were made in Paris. The MAISON PATHÉ produced a catalogue of more than 100 Yvette Guilbert cylinders, which afford a pano-ramic view of Guilbert's talent. Among those responsible for her material were Leon Xanrof, Jules Jouy, Maurice Donnay, Jean Richepin, Aristide Bruant, Jules Moy, Fragson, and, of course Yvette Guilbert herself. This series must have begun in 1899 with what collectors call 'one at a time' recordings on yellow wax, continuing after 1900 on moulded cylinders in black wax. Standard, Inter and Stentor size records figured in the list, and after 1906 re-issues on sapphire records were sold in various guises. Exceptionally attrac-tive though these PATHÉ records are, sales were not very large and it is very hard to form a collection.

Indefatigably Yvette Guilbert continued her career and with it her record-ing. Another company for whom she worked in Edwardian days was the COMPAGNIE FRANÇAISE DU GRAMOPHONE; in 1904 she sang twelve sides for them, including 'Le Fiacre' again and some Bruant numbers. The outbreak of war brought no interruption. The public needed amusement; besides, Guilbert was much concerned with Red Cross and other social work. In 1915, she married an American and sailed for the United States where she was to remain for seven years. She took up lecturing and teaching in addition to her concert career. During 1918, she made more records in New York, this time for COLUMBIA; the twelve sides included items from her usual repertoire, and also for the first time medieval songs, and *'Ma grand'mère'* by Béranger.

YVETTE GUILBERT

Yvette Guilbert and her famous black gloves. Her long career as a star embraced the cylinder, the disc, and even the beginnings of electric recording.

Among the various caricatures drawn by Caruso, his sketch of Yvette Guilbert takes a high place. It was drawn in 1908.

On her return to Europe, Guilbert was as busy as ever. Visiting England in 1928, she made three double-sided records for GRAMOPHONE. These were her first electrical recordings. Composers ranged from Adam de la Halle to Léon Xanrof, and also included traditional songs. Untiring but no longer as slim as she had been, Yvette Guilbert continued her worldwide platform appearances. At 66 she was back in the recording studio, re-making most of the old favourites, her presentation as sprightly and diction as crisp as ever. On these records, as on those made for PATHÉ in 1900, Yvette Guilbert announced the song title before the music began. These discs date from 1933/1934. There are eleven of them, and they are collectable, too, for the work of Guilbert's accompanist, Irène Aïtof. The principal hits in this series were *Le Fiacre, Madame Arthur, L'hôtel du N° 3*, and *La Complainte des quatr'z Étudiants*.

With these records one might expect Yvette Guilbert's career to have reached its end; but not so! Ten years later, shortly before her death in 1944 at Aix-en-Provence, she recorded (for broadcasting) songs by Béranger, poems and an artistic testament. These last Guilbert recordings were issued only in micro-groove.

Motion pictures too, attracted Yvette Guilbert. She acted in several films and also made discs intended as sound tracks in the early days of talkies. CINÉDISC was the name of this film company, and the records were produced by the FRENCH RECORDING COMPANY, 12 boulevard de la Madeleine, Paris. Titles included *Les Cloches de Nantes* and *Le joli Tambour*, two traditional songs.

The titles alone of Yvette Guilbert's records would lead one to suppose that they meant something in her life. Her memoirs do not mention them, but one has only to hear one of her numbers to realise that the quality is there.

ORCHESTRAL   On the earliest records the words of songs were not always perfectly clear. In his first catalogue (1890) Thomas A. Edison offered instrumental solos: piano, flute, clarinet, bassoon and cornet. Instruments came out better than singing. An early problem to be solved was the recording of several instruments together; then came the question of a whole orchestra, which was not really resolved until the arrival of microphones and electrical recording. Makers soon learned that wind instruments suited the cylinder phonograph because their bells could be aimed directly into the recording horn, and thus reach the diaphragm. The popularity of brass bands meant that current favourites could be captured, starting with national anthems and marches, and moving from there to dance music — waltzes, mazurkas, polkas and schottisches. Many were the arrangements for wind instruments alone, and the champion in this field, without any doubt, was the band of the *Garde Républicaine* . The number of cylinders and discs made by this orchestra for a variety of companies is incalculable. PATHÉ publicity contained the following letter from M. Pares, the bandmaster:

'I testify that the scores necessary to the performance of the musical works contained in the present catalogue were orchestrated and played under my direction by the best soloists in the band of the *Garde Républicaine*, notably Messieurs Lachanaud, Fontbonne, Paradis, Barthélemy, Strady, etc... etc..., ... for the Etablissements PATHÉ FRÈRES.'

Paris, 16 March, 1900
Signed: Pares.

This letter helps to explain the multitude of recordings. The full strength of the *Musique de la Garde* was 70 musicians or thereabouts; splitting these up into small units enabled the number of recordings to be multiplied; and the fact that ten was the largest group that could be recorded explains a great deal.

Large symphony orchestras could in no way be captured by a single recording horn. It was not possible to group thirty or forty violins; and so we find arrangements for wind instruments alone playing havoc with famous overtures and andante movements. By the same token, ensembles for *trompes de chasse* were favourites for recording, although long-held notes had a tendency to bleat owing to variations in speed.

Present day bandsmen in the *Musique de la Garde* sigh for those days of repetitive acoustic recording. Brass meant 'brass' in those days and it does not rain in the studio, which is more than can be said for the parade ground...

The band of the French Republican Guard, drawn up for an official photograph. The limitations of the early recording methods were such that the band in its entirety was too much for the apparatus, and so only sections of the band were recorded on any one cylinder.

Musique de la Garde-Républicaine
Chef: Mr Gabriel PARÈS

Ch. Debrock   Reproduction interdite

Musicians jammed up close in an early recording studio, with their conductor badly placed out of their natural line of sight. Thousands of orchestral recordings were made under such difficult conditions.

The caricature, which appeared in *Le Pêle-Mêle* of 21 April 1901, poked fun at the invisible orchestras that were heard on recordings. The scruffy collection in the drawing is pretending to be the Royal Danish orchestra.

CHEZ LE FABRICANT D'APPAREILS PHONOGRAPHIQUES

On enregistre des rouleaux de phonographes.

LE MUSICIEN *(criant dans l'appareil)*. — *Le Beau Danube bleu*, exécuté par la musique royale de Danemark.

The *Ménestrel* — 'Minstrel' — was specially made for a credit sales company, J. Girard et Cie of Paris. The machine used the mechanical parts of the Pathé *Le Gaulois* model. The 1902 version was painted blue and gold, and the diaphragm was the Pathé *Rex*.

CREDIT SALES

After a few months, the blue *Ménestrel* was replaced by the same model painted in green and gold. The new *Ménestrel* was equipped with a system that also allowed it to play intermediate-size cylinders, and the diaphragm was the Pathé *Coq* in ebonite.

The high cost of the early phonographs limited their sale. GRAPHOPHONE in the States and PATHÉ in France brought out simplified models at reasonable prices. Also the method of payment by monthly instalments, which had existed for several years, was applied to the talking machine. In France this became the province of specialised finance houses.

Messrs. E. Girard & A. Boitte, 42 rue de l'Echiquier, Paris, had been selling books, lamps, ornaments, etc. 'by easy payments' for some while when they added phonographs to their list early in 1899. Their name for the first model offered was *Le Tonnerre*, although it was really an *Eagle*, with hardly any change. *Girard et Boitte* advertised widely in the press and they certainly beat the drum, whether one believes them or not:

'Le *Tonnerre* is supplied complete with two soundboxes, for recording and playing respectively. UNIQUE in being fitted with dual rubber tubes and four Ear-pieces in Ebonite for personal auditions. UNIQUE in affording perfect speed control. UNIQUE in being sold with 25 Blank cylinders on which Customers may record as many impressions as they wish... Price 147 Francs payable over 21 months at the rate of 7 francs a month'. The text also states that '4000 machines are in the course of manufacture'. One imagines that this figure was somewhat exaggerated. At the end of 1899 the firm was reconstructed and became J. GIRARD ET CIE, SUCCESSEURS DE E. GIRARD ET A. BOITTE. The machine offered at the old price of 147 francs, was called *Omega*. It was unusual in having a vertical governor. Equally 'amazing and sublime', as the vendors called all their machines, was the *Ménestrel*, of 1900. This marked the start of a PATHÉ connexion, the *Ménestrel* being none other than a PATHÉ *Gaulois*. Originally this came in a rectangular box; later the lid was domed. The base of the machine itself was blue, with gold lines. The trumpet was metallized glass. The price was still 147 francs but the 25 cylinders now comprised 20 records and only five blanks.

A second model was offered in 1902 'in the style of Louis XV', with cast-iron base and metal lid, the whole instrument painted blue and lined outlined in gold. This model does not appear in PATHÉ's own list, although the motor was from one of their models. Only standard (54 mm diameter) cylinders could be played on this machine. Towards the end of the same year there appeared another 'Louis XV' phonograph, painted green and taking 90 mm cylinders as well. All this for the same 147 francs, complete with 10 large cylinders, 10 small, and 5 blanks. How stable prices were in those days!

GIRARD ET CIE, then, were granted exclusive rights to credit trading by PATHÉ FRÈRES. From 1903 they might sell machines identical with those sold by PATHÉ direct. And with the new arrangement came an Exceptional Offer. The phonograph itself was given away for nothing, and only the records sold 'on the never-never': 100 cylinders for 150 francs, payable over 20 months at 7.50 francs a month. After October 1903, customers could have *Système Vérité* soundbox etc., although this was a little dearer: 225 francs spread over 25 months for 100 cylinders, but these were the large 90 mm ones.

The *Chante-Clair* phonograph came out in 1904, and when PATHÉ changed to flat records J. GIRARD ET CIE continued to handle credit sales, from 1906. Each new machine was sold with a large number of records. In 1909, by some quirk the firm once more became GIRARD ET BOITTE, without initials but with the addition of *seuls concessionnaires pour la vente à terme*. With the outbreak of war in 1914, a gramophone craze set in, and easy terms were no longer worth while. The advertising lost some of its energy too.

GIRARD ET BOITTE were the pioneers of 'pay as you play'. Next came a provincial house, G. Maleville, publisher of Libourne (Gironde), who already sold books, cameras, bicycles, pianos and musical instruments. At the end of 1899 he offered *Le Virtuose du Foyer* (the Home Virtuoso). 'The improved French phonograph' he called it, though it was really a GRAPHOPHONE *Eagle* copy... 130 francs at 6.50 a month for the machine and 10 cylinders. One suspects that this machine was made by J. THIBOUVILLE-LAMY ET CIE, for it had been advertised by them in 1898. By 1901, it was the turn of *Le Phenix* 'Wonder of the World'. There were several versions: the original which took standard 50 mm cylinders, one to take two sizes, and a third playing only *Phenix* 80 mm cylinders, made originally of yellow wax, later black. Maleville also retailed the *Excelsior* phonograph, not to be confused with the German machine of the same name.

In 1905 he advertised *Musica* phonographs manufactured by G. Dutreih with 50 cylinders. *Maleville* had branches in Paris, at 104, rue de Richelieu (in 1899) then at 66, rue de Rivoli, at 10 allée de Tourny, Bordeaux, and 59, rue du Midi, Brussels.

Among other French firms selling cylinder machines on credit and the machines they sold, the following may be mentioned:

— *Le Sublime* from Rivemale-Rives 156/158, rue Rivoli, Paris

— *Le Sonor* from the shop 'Aux Canotiers' 13, avenue Lamotte Picquet, Paris

— *Prométhée* from M. Danvers, 15, rue de Maubeuge, Paris

— *Paris-Phonographe* from Comptoir Universel de France, 60, rue de Provence, Paris

— *Le Charmeur* from the Librairie des Chansons Illustrées, 8, rue Saint-Joseph, Paris

J. Girard offered the Pathé machine under the ▶ tradename of *Sonor* in 1903. In 1904 it became the *Vérité*. The *Vérité* horn support system gave the machine the breath of life, the advertisements boasted.

154

With the coming of flat records credit sales rather tailed off, although as we have seen GIRARD did persevere on behalf of PATHÉ. Others were:

— *Phrynis* from the Librairie des Connaissances Utiles, 21, rue du Pont Neuf, Paris

— *Aspir* from Les Etablissements Phonographiques d'Ivry, 5, rue Boudreau, Paris

— *Morelophone* from Le Comptoir Général du Phonographe, 10, rue Montgolfier, Paris.

Prominent amongst manufacturers not prone to grant easy terms was the COMPAGNIE FRANÇAISE DU GRAMOPHONE, which relied on other promotional means.

The improved *Phenix* of 1904. A rigid support bar allowed the horn and diaphragm to float. The graduated speed control remained.

The phonograph given away free with 100 cylinders had a white, wooden case covered with paper, but the same mechanism as the phonographs sold at the normal price.

In order to sell off as quickly as possible the small cylinders which were about to be replaced with the larger size, a French credit sales company offered the old versions in lots of 100 cylinders, with a phonograph thrown in for nothing. This was at the beginning of 1903. However, it was necessary to change the sales message and continue with 100 large cylinders, since Pathé made a bid to corner the French market with the larger size.

◄ Left: The *Phenix*, distributed in the provinces by Maleville of Libourne, played ordinary cylinders until 1902. The 1903 model, which came out in October 1902, only took the larger cylinders of the same make. Though large, their dimension was a few millimetres smaller than the standard 'intermediate' cylinder.

Phonographs and their Uses

It is something of a paradox that the poet Charles Cros produced a technical description devoted to the process of recording sounds, while Thomas Alva Edison from his very first patents imagined a vast number of applications open to his phonograph. Following the invention and development of the telephone, it seemed a natural derivation to associate the phonograph with it to record calls. However, this application had no future with acoustic recording, and had to wait for the development of the magnetic recorder before it had any practical use. Progress made in cylinder materials, and in phonograph mechanisms enabled the invention to be commercialized seriously after 1888. Technical difficulties sometimes baffled the ideas of the makers, and lines too hastily embarked upon were as quickly abandoned (Edison's talking doll, for example). The high price of the early phonographs effectively prevented them from becoming popular, and so coin-operated machines which quickly recovered their initial costs, found an expanding market.

COIN-OPERATED PHONOGRAPHS

◄ A café table containing a coin-operated phonograph. It boasted a selection of twelve cylinders, which rotated with their mandrels until the chosen recording reached the fixed diaphragm. The mechanism was set going by means of a token. The ones used for this ancestor of the juke box bear an address in Belleville, Paris, and the machine was in use there in about 1910. The cardboard disc was printed with figures that corresponded to the cylinders, and the chosen number appeared in a small window on the tabletop. The performance was heard through a small earphone on the end of a flexible tube.

Thomas Edison led the way by charging an entrance fee to the demonstrations he organised at exhibitions. The novelty of the invention appealed to the public taste, and long queues to hear recordings influenced eventual buyers. The organisation of these demonstrations necessitated a large staff to work the machines, and thus to be a paying proposition, the phonograph needed to be equipped with an automatic system which would enable them to play when a coin or a previously purchased token was introduced. Once this system was perfected, coin-operated phonographs quickly became a feature of cafés and public places. The GRAPHOPHONE Company was the first to offer robust, simple-to-operate phonographs at a realistic price. The *Eagle* and *Model A* machines took the name *Coin-Slot Graphophones*, and were either supplied with a horn, or with individual earphones (which brought in more money since the number of listeners at any one time was restricted). World-wide distribution of these models started in 1898 and was well-received. Smaller makers imitated the principle, and soon it seemed that any phonograph or gramophone could be converted into coin- or token-operated machines. The manufacturers saw these machines as good publicity for their wares, and thus gave special terms to buyers of coin-operated phonographs.

159

A very rare coin-operated *Gramophone*, which had the same mechanics as the standard machine, and which took bronze 10 centime pieces. It played small, 17 cm (6.6 in) records, which were stored in a compartment in the gramophone case. Left: A notice explaining the operation of the machine, and warning customers to change the needle for each record.

The idea of public entertainment by coin-operated gramophone quickly caught on, and many manufacturers produced their own variations on a theme. The gramophone illustrated is a *Ramophone*, sold by a French provincial firm. The machine, with its large brass horn, was made in about 1910. Left: Details of the turntable and diaphragm.

160

The Bussoz firm of Paris still exists, and still sells juke-boxes, very unlike the large automatic gramophone shown here. This machine had a range of shelves which stocked twenty records. The turntable, balanced by a counter-weight, sank down, the chosen record slid out of its shelf onto the turntable, which then rose to the playing position. When the record was finished the whole operation took place in reverse.

Right: A similar machine to the *Ramophone*, the *Concert Automatique Français* differed only in the style of the cabinet, which had a sliding front. The coin-operated machines of the time played hill-and-dale records, since the sapphire needle used for this type of recording was less liable to wear.

Far right: An electric-powered coin-operated gramophone with wooden earphones. The mechanism and the coinbox can be seen through the bevelled glass panels. There are no distinguishing marks to identify the machine.

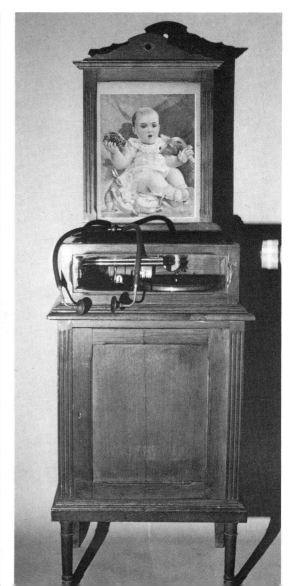

The first experiments in sound recording were made with the human voice. Thus, no doubt, Edison naturally saw a use for the invention as a dictation machine. It was possible to dictate letters at the normal rate of speech, after which a secretary could transcribe the letters while listening to the cylinder, stopping it at will. Some years were needed before the system became a practical proposition. An electric motor was necessary in order not to lose time in winding up clockwork. The 2 volt batteries of the time were not too reliable, and so it was essential to await the development of electric motors using mains current before the office machine could be fully exploited. Hill-and-dale recording, whether on cylinders or discs, was the only type offered with the simple and robust machines meant to be used by non-technical persons. Disc dictating machines, even using the hill-and-dale principle, were rare, and it was more usual to find cylinder machines which used thick 15 cm (5.9 in.) cylinders which could have the recording planed off for re-use.

Dictating machines did not have a spectacular horn, and were constructed in a functional manner, and are thus less sought after by collectors.

PHONOGRAPHS IN THE OFFICE

Courtesy
Antique Phonograph Monthly

Dictating to the *Graphophone*.

Courtesy
Antique Phonograph Monthly

Transcribing from the *Graphophone*.

Left and right: The *Parlograph* dictating machine was probably of American origin, and was sold in various countries. It carried a plate which gave the patent numbers and occasionally the name of the local agent. The machine shown here is marked Patent SGDG No. 415911. The diaphragm allowed both recording and playing, thanks to interchangeable sapphire needles. The recording trumpet is in painted aluminium.

The *Roneophone* was the result of collaboration between the Pathé and Roneo firms. The dictating machine used a thick wax disc. After each recording the disc could be shaved down to remove the message, reducing its thickness each time. On the right of the picture can be seen the speaking-tube and trumpet linked to the recording diaphragm, on the left the earphones connected to the playing diaphragm. It was powered by an electric motor.
Below left: Detail of the *Roneophone*.

Right: The *Dictaphone* Model *10* Type *B* was a dictating machine made in the United States. The machine illustrated is the playback machine for the secretary, which played cylinders previously recorded on another machine. The small flat lever moved the diaphragm back a few grooves to repeat a phrase. A tube, leading to two earphones, fitted on the diaphragm.

Below left: The *Ediphone* dictating machine on its metal base, which served as a store for the cylinders. Thomas Edison made business machines from 1889 until 1929, and some of his dictating machines were in use up to the Second World War. The machine shown below was one of the last he made. It would play the cylinders but not record them — the recording version of the *Ediphone* was needed for that.

Below right: An Edison-made device for planing off recordings from the cylinders used in the dictating machines. A cylinder was placed on the mandrel and a very thin layer of wax removed from the circumference. *Ediphone* cylinders were thicker than the usual cylinders to allow for this treatment.

Although cylinder phonographs offered anyone the chance to record, and one might feel that the proliferation of phonographs would mean that the opportunity to exchange messages would take on a certain importance, in practice several snags arose. It was difficult to be sure of making a satisfactory recording, for in general phonographs on sale were much inferior to the machines used for professional recording. Again, the vocal technique was such that only a few professional artistes of the time possessed it. Finally, the transport of the very fragile cylinders posed a problem. In contrast to dictating machines, message-taking phonographs were nearly always disc machines. The *Phonopostal* was a small machine, giving only mediocre results, but which used special postcards which could be recorded on, and which were generally held to be a charming idea. The Pathé firm went one better in launching the *Pathépost*, which used small discs. The model continued in production for several years, and after the First World War, the name was changed to *Pathégraph* — not to be confused with the *Pathégraphe* language tutor.

MESSAGE-TAKING PHONOGRAPHS

An advertisement for the *Phonopostal* system (1906), which enabled recordings to be made and posted, in the form of postcards. Unfortunately, the metal parts that enabled the recordings to be moulded at medium heat often bent and broke, particularly the cardholder, so that it is rare to find a *Phonopostal* complete and in good condition.

The *Pathépost*, was used with special discs of 11 cm (4.3 in) and 14 cm (5.5 in) in diameter, which could be placed in special envelopes for posting. It seems that the first *Pathépost* machines came out in about 1908, but they did not enjoy a great success.

LANGUAGE TUTORS

Pronounciation difficulties in learning foreign languages seemed likely to be overcome by the use of a phonograph, which, after all, was conceived to repeat the same sounds time and again. There were a number of recordings made, which, with the aid of a handbook, enabled the student to quickly learn Russian, French, German, Esperanto or... English. Cylinders could be recorded by the student, permitting him to check on his pronounciation and his progress at the same time. The NORTH AMERICAN PHONOGRAPH CO. in 1893 was already selling cylinders recording Greek, Latin, French, German and Spanish phrases following Dr Richard S. Rosenthal's methods. In 1912, the PATHÉ firm once again produced an astonishing invention: the *Pathégraphe*, an audio-visual method for learning foreign languages. Nowadays, the defects of the system can be more clearly seen; the size of the machine, the number of records (26/35 cm — 14 in — discs), and 26 printed paper rolls.

Engravings showing the recording of a language text on an Edison *M* machine, and it being checked back by means of earphones afterwards. *La Nature,* September 1893.

The plate on the gramophone on the right stated in French that the machine was made for the International Schools, Paris, for the study of living languages. Recordings on discs could be made by means of the special arm to which was attached the recording diaphragm, which moved steadily forward guided by a rack and pinion. Play-back was through a cloth speaker incorporated in the case.

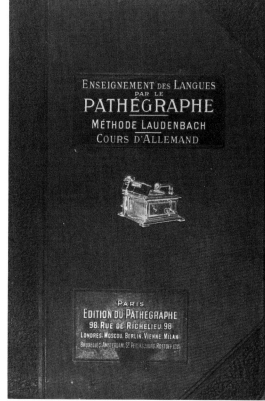

The *Pathégraphe* of 1913. A roll of paper was synchronised with the record, enabling the lesson to be read while listening to the disc. The translation was printed on the top of the roll, and could be covered by the folding *Pathégraphe* plate. One handle wound up the motor, the other the roll. The gramophone part was a *Pathé-reflex*, with a horn incorporated in the lid.

TALKING CLOCKS

The *Peter Pan* alarm clock was an extremely simple device. After winding up the clock and the gramophone motor, the alarm was set to the desired hour, and the needle placed in the first groove on the record, which started playing when the set time arrived. The alarm was patented and sold in France, but had a Swiss motor and diaphragm. About 1930.

To wake up to music has always been one of man's fantasies, and the gramophone seemed to be an economical way to realise this. About 1906, the first phono-alarm clock was made in Germany, known as the *Tempophon*, which, governed by a clock, played at a previously set hour. Later, in 1925, the *Peter Pan Clock* was produced which worked on exactly the same principle as the German machine. However, both these machines were only gramophones controlled by a clock. A Berlin maker, Hiller, produced the first talking clock in 1911. He could have used a disc, but instead used a perforated celluloid film, with the time recorded on it, which was read by a diaphragm which travelled across the film. There were 48 positions, which corresponded to the hours, half-hours and quarters in a twelve-hour span.

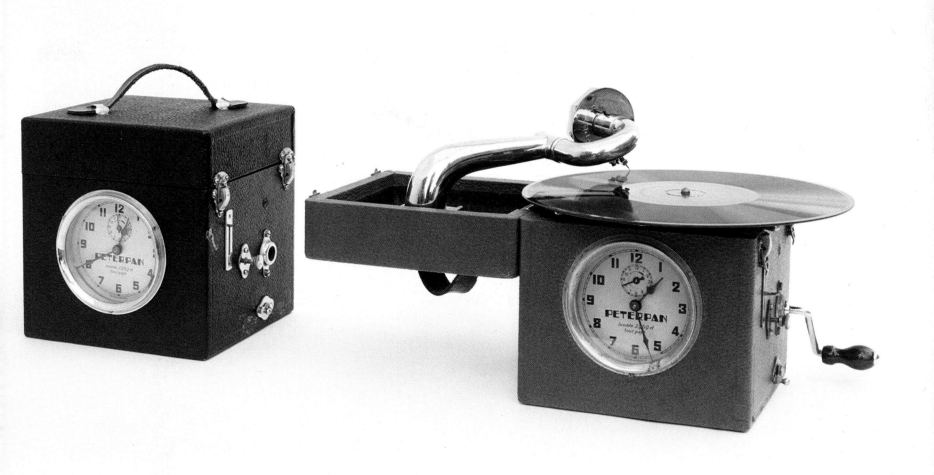

A clock by Hiller. In 1911, B. Hiller built in Berlin a clock which contained a film upon which 48 tracks were recorded giving the time every quarter of an hour from midday to midnight. When a button was pressed, the film started, and the track was played by a diaphragm and amplified by the small white trumpet. This clock spoke German, but it was possible to record in other languages. Left: Detail of the mechanism.

Another clock by Hiller. The one shown below is in stained wood, while the first was in mahogany. The film recording was vertical, and a device enabled the time to be repeated several times — no doubt for use as an alarm clock.

TOY PHONOGRAPHS

The manufacture of toy phonographs for children opened up a large field for constructors. Hand-cranked toys were made by Berliner in 1889, then by others, but without great commercial success, since the crude machinery only gave a distorted result. Phonographs made for the popular market were already made as simply as possible in order to keep the price down, so how were cheap toys to be made? The Germans, already ahead in the tin toy trade, came up with the answer. The peak of German manufacture was between 1925 and 1940. The small motors, extensively mass-produced, were the weak points of their toys, the sound equipment being greatly superior. In the doll world, after the Edison experiments in 1888/89, after the success of Henri Lioret's *Bébés Jumeau*, after the German dolls with wax cylinders and the Averill *Mae Starr* dolls in the United States, the popularity of the talking doll had to wait for the advent of the transistor and electronics.

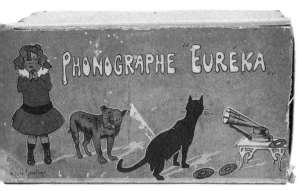

The *Eureka* gramophone, made in Germany, played chocolate gramophone records. Various chocolate makers, such as Stollwerck in Belgium, used the machine in their publicity. The turntable was a box to hold several discs.

The famous German toymakers Bing had a department that made children's gramophones. Generally, they were in painted sheet metal. The *Pygmophone* below had the horn fixed directly to the diaphragm.

The *Gamaphola* was another Bing offering, with jazz-age decorations painted on the sheet metal. The base of the gramophone served as a soundbox.

◄ Left: The German makers, Nier and Ehmer, put out the *Nirona Suzy*, with a bell-shaped soundbox which was typical of the make. The model was sold in France for 120 francs in 1929, being reduced to 99 in 1932. The *Nirona* came packed in a cardboard box (above) which showed adults dancing to the gramophone — no doubt an attempt to flatter what was basically a children's toy.

Another toy gramophone from Bing, known as the *Garmanette*. The holes in the turntable were for the winding key.

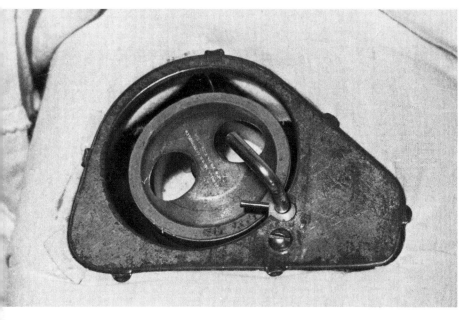

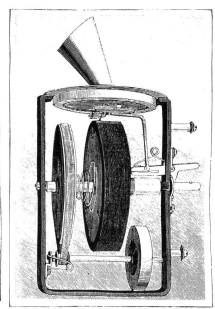

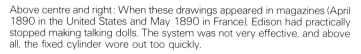

Above centre and right: When these drawings appeared in magazines (April 1890 in the United States and May 1890 in France), Edison had practically stopped making talking dolls. The system was not very effective, and above all, the fixed cylinder wore out too quickly.

Left: A more modern doll (about 1930) than the one shown below, made in the United States and 75 cms (29.5 in) tall. The phonograph mechanism is marked Averill Manufacturing Co., New York City, USA. The doll, which has closing eyes, is marked behind the head 'Mae Starr Doll'. The cylinder is sky blue, and the trumpet is concealed in the breast. Above left: A detail of the mechanism.

Below: An American doll with head, arms and legs in papier mâché and a cloth body. A phonograph was inserted into the body with the horn in the head. The dark blue, celluloid cylinder was reinforced with a cardboard ring. The doll was 55 cm (21.6 in) high.

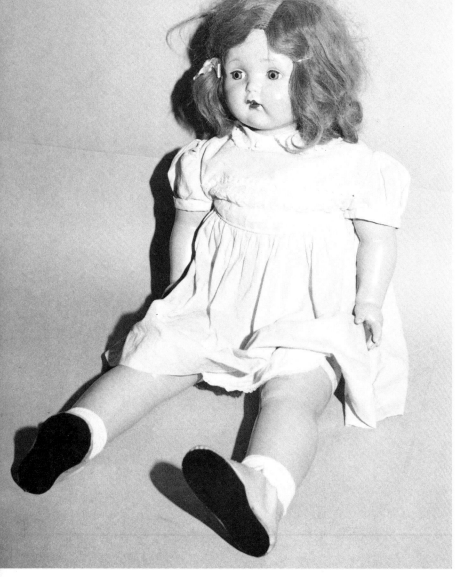

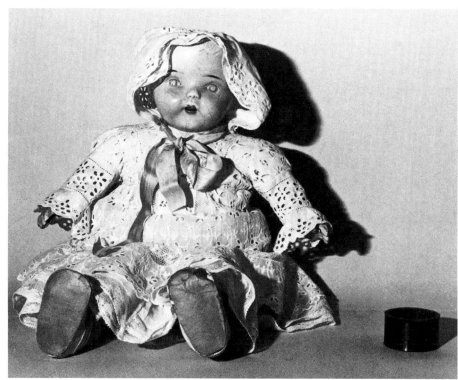

PHONOGRAPHIC GADGETS

The first concealed phonographs were hidden in the bodies of dolls. With the development of the disc-playing gramophone, large horns proliferated for a while until the fashion passed, and the public demanded soundboxes hidden in the gramophone cabinet. Carrying this situation still further, several makers argued that perhaps it was better to make gramophones that did not look like gramophones at all. Thus machines appeared that looked like suitcases, vanity bags, and even hat boxes (the portable *Odéon*), not counting the innumerable fake cameras or piles of books gutted to take a gramophone. Thus it is possible to understand that the idea came to some manufacturers to use a large lamp-shade to conceal their machines. Probably the example in the worst taste was the so-called 'work of art' — Buddha with a gramophone in his belly.

The three old books conceal a Paillard gramophone powered by the Swiss-made motor No. 55. The diaphragm could be adapted to play either needle or sapphire lateral or vertical records.

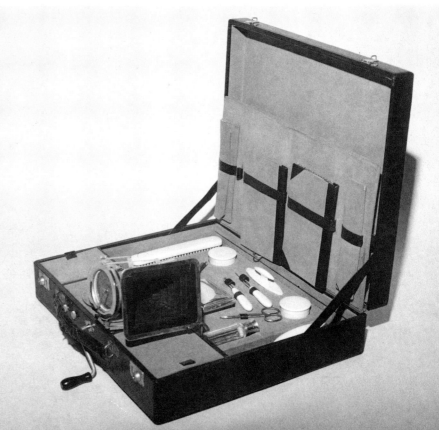

The travelling case contained toilet articles, writing paper and a gramophone. The *Triumphone* was equipped with a horn that folded like a bellows camera. It was French-made.

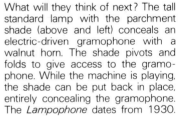

What will they think of next? The tall standard lamp with the parchment shade (above and left) conceals an electric-driven gramophone with a walnut horn. The shade pivots and folds to give access to the gramophone. While the machine is playing, the shade can be put back in place, entirely concealing the gramophone. The *Lampophone* dates from 1930.

A certain G.G. de Andia-Yrarrazaval took out a patent in London on 20 March 1923, and again on 20 September 1924, for a gramophone horn concealed inside a statuette. One of the results was the Confucious gramophone, marked *Vocalion, Andia registered patent*.

Another of Andia's gramophones in doubtful taste. The example below is labelled as an 'artistic phonograph', and is said to come from Paris and Brussels. Below left: Buddha concealing the works. Below right: Buddha turned over for playing with the diaphragm fixed to the centre of the statuette base. The gramophone could be had with an electric motor if required.

The mysteries of the diaphragm, the little box that reads and amplifies sounds, caught the imagination of secondary inventors. A German, Augustus Stroh, living in London from 1851, was interested by the first struggles of the phonograph, and being an excellent mechanic, built several machines after 1878, particularly a machine, driven by a weight, which engraved on pewter. In 1899, Stroh took out a patent, which he completed in 1901, for a special type of violin in which the strings were amplified by a diaphragm attached to a trumpet. There was an immediate use for this unlikely successor to the work of Stradivarius: the making of phonograph recordings. The sound of a violin was very difficult to record, but with Stroh's invention, the trumpet could be pointed at the recording horn. Later, many clowns delighted the public with their antics with a Stroh violin or its derivations. They were also occasionally used in jazz bands, being then known as 'phono-fiddles'.

STROH VIOLINS

A violin, or phonofiddle, constructed on the Stroh principle. It was made by the famous Paris musical instrument maker Couesnon, who specialised in brass and woodwind instruments.

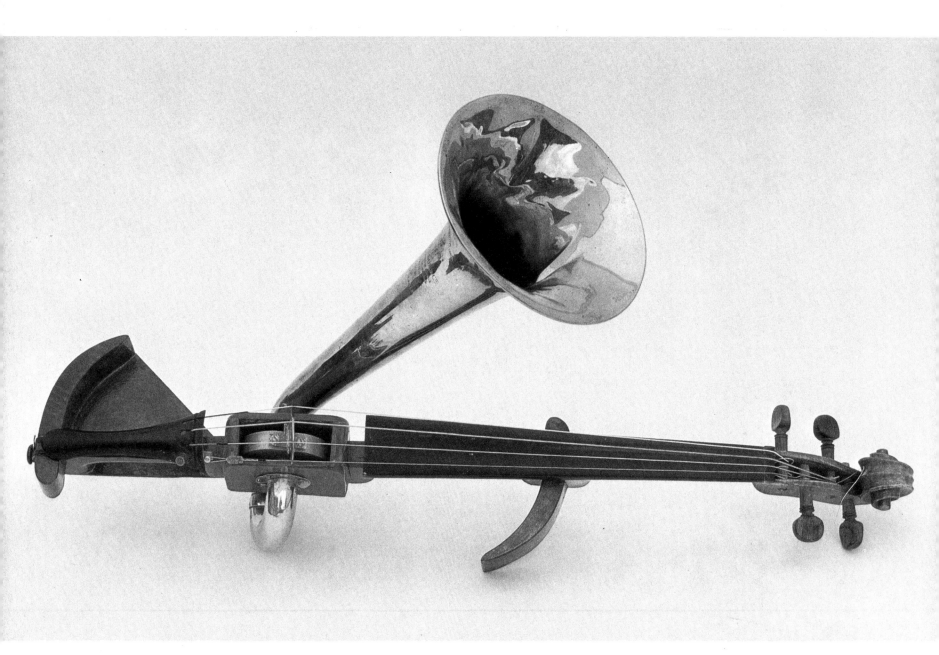

178

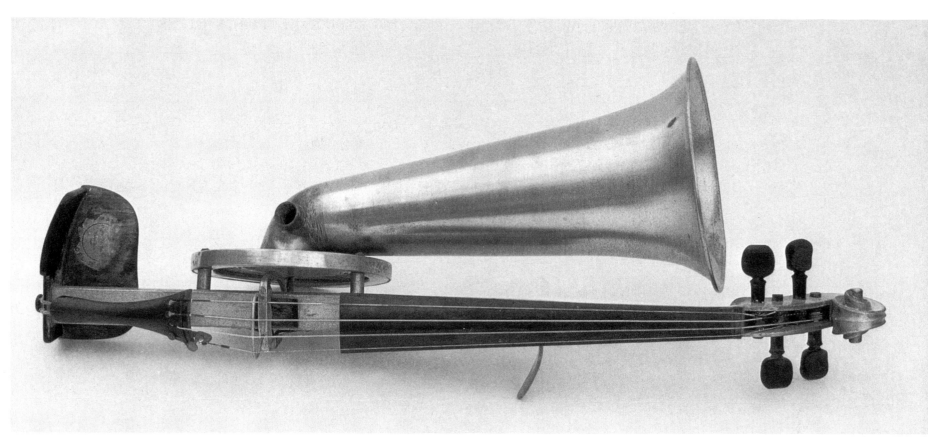

A violin with a large aluminium diaphragm, made in Germany and stamped Tiebel Violine D.R.W. 2 355993.
The instrument carries a label from a shop in Salonika.

The 'cello below is marked 'Concert Model British Manufacture'. It was intended to be clasped between the knees
and played with a bow. It seems unlikely to have been very musical, since it only had one string.

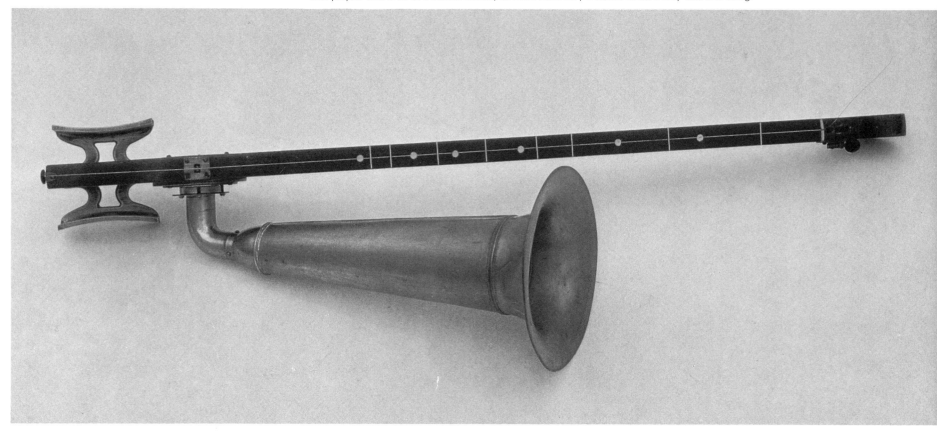

Phonographic Accessories

The commercial competition that involved turn-of-the-century phonograph makers led them to try to distinguish themselves either in accessory details or in an original style, even though the machines themselves were plagiarized, not only technically, but even, to make confusion worse, in name: *Gramophone, Grimophone* and *Graphophone* are very close! However, it was not so difficult to produce a tin of needles or a cylinder tube that differed from others on the market. Record sleeves were also a good publicity aid. Nellie Melba's records came out in 1904 with a cover printed in golden letters, and bearing a photograph of the great Australian singer. *Fonotipia* also produced sleeves with portraits of some of their artistes. Then as now, when antistatic dusters and electric cleaners are offered for LPs, there were a number of gadgets available, some useful, others the contrary. Nearly all discs, whether for sapphire or for needle playing, were advertised as impossible to wear out, yet a number of creams were offered at the same time to prevent their doing so — a useful commercial paradox!

NEEDLE TINS

The round-headed sapphire used for hill-and-dale recordings on both cylinders and discs was practically impossible to wear out, and care only had to be taken not to drop and break it. Records to be played by needle were best heard when a sharp steel needle was used and changed for each side. The diameter and length of the needle modified the strength of the sound, which necessitated various needles according to the recording, and these were sold as soft, medium, strong and very strong. The hardness of the metal used could also vary the length of time they could be used; there were permanent points, semi-permanent, 10, 50 or 100 playing types. It will be seen later that there were needles that could be resharpened to extend their playing life. Needle boxes came with all sorts of labels; some advertised makes of gramophones, others big shops, while the quantity of figures and designs makes it impossible to set down a list, so many were they. Some designs, be it noted in passing, seemed to have had little to do with the contents: a seal, a lion, a bishop or a clown.

◄ An assortment of boxes of gramophone needles. German manufacturers dominated the European market, but each gramophone manufacturer had a tendency to bring out his own brand of needles.

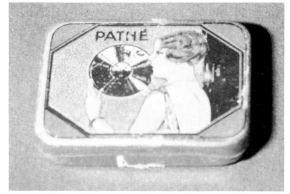

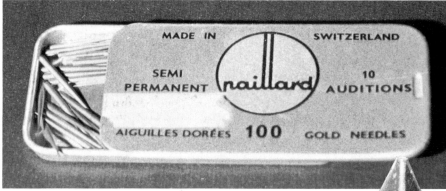

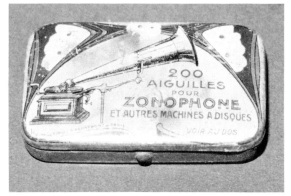

Pathé's tin of needles carried a very 'thirties illustration, while *Zonophone* showed a handsome gramophone. The pyramid distributed needles one by one through a small hole at its apex. The Gramophone company marked its products with its famous dog but, as can be seen, there were some fairly close imitations.

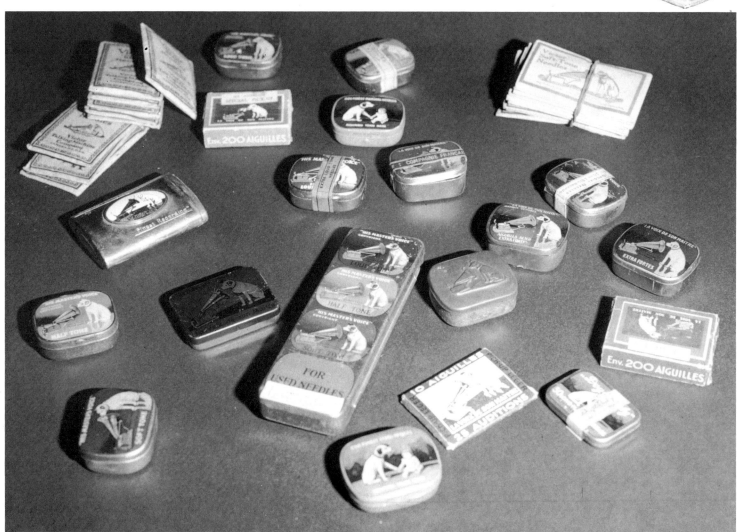

NEEDLE SHARPENERS

When a record started to sound badly, it was often due to needle wear, which in turn reacted on the grooves. By using a new needle for each playing, its wear was limited. There was another possibility: the use of a less hard material than steel, and wooden, fibre, bamboo and quill needles, etc. were produced. With characteristic carefulness, the British demanded needles that were kind to their records — one of the reasons why England is the country where the oldest records are best preserved, to the pleasure of the collector.

Soft needles needed frequent sharpening. Triangular bamboo needles were split by a special pair of pliers, and fibre needles were sharpened on a piece of emery paper. The ingenuity of the makers was astonishing. In 1907, a patent was taken out in the USA for bamboo needles. Soft points did not always stand up to very pronounced grooves for loud or sharp sounds, and the playing was liable to end in a rude noise. Of course, this risk is still present today if a worn sapphire or diamond is used on a microgroove record.

An English-made needle sharpener. A circle of emery paper which rubbed against the needle gave a perfectly sharp point.

Bamboo needles were celebrated for their tone, but they needed frequent recutting. *His Master's Voice* supplied a machine for this purpose.

183

There is more interest today in an exact reproduction of old records than seemed to be the case at the beginning of the century. Recording machines did not always turn at the same speeds, while the playing machines were not at all precise, so that there could be a vast difference between the sound recorded and the sound played back. Acceleration raised the note, slowing down lowered it. A book published in 1965 analysed all the recordings made by Caruso. Speed was far from being constant: 75 rpm for *Zonophone* records, 71 rpm for the first *Gramophones*, and 67 rpm for those made in November 1902. Imagine how the great tenor sounded played at 78 rpm! Today it is imagined that all wax records are 78s, but nothing could be further from the truth. The sapphire Pathés had a speed varying between 80 to 120 rpm. A stroboscope used in conjunction with an electric light gave a precise indication of the speed of rotation, while certain gramophones were equipped with a graduated speed gauge.

Every collector should be aware of the speed problem, and take into account the transpositions that singers frequently used. Still the best method to use is the stroboscope.

The Paillard speed gauge was easy to operate. The far end of the device was placed over the stud in the centre of the turntable, and the machine was switched on. When the turntable reached 78 rpm, the arm descended horizontally to face the mark on the pillar.

CYLINDER BOXES

The advantage of the cylinder is that the diameter of the groove is constant, contrasting with that of the disc. The great drawback of the cylinder is its fragility, and the difficulty in storing it. Whether engraved or moulded, once made, the cylinder had to be transported, and thus felt-lined cardboard tubes were used. What was unknown at the time was that the cylinders were sensitive to damp, and the felt encouraged the growth of fungus, which ate into the playing surface, and produced a roughening which translated into a horrible noise when the cylinder was played.

Lioret's unbreakable cylinders were packed in unlined boxes. The large Stentor cylinders were inserted into boxes with a mandrel that kept the playing surface out of contact with the sides of the tube. Decoration of the tubes was usually limited to a label stuck on the top, but Edison always had his portrait and trademark on the tube.

There were innumerable cylinder types and labels. Phonograph makes, shops and distributors, wax makers, all had their own brand.

The four sizes of Lioret cylinders: No. 1 length 1.7 cm (0.6 in), playing time 30 secs.
No. 2 length 2.4 cm (0.9 in), playing time 1 min.
No. 3 length 4 cm (1.6 in), playing time 2 min.
No. 4 length 8 cm (3.2 in), playing time 4 min.

The printing and decoration of cylinder tubes reflected the taste of the 1900s.

DISCS   Collecting old records deserves a book to itself. Just think of the marvels which have been preserved on wax since the invention of the phonograph — composers playing their own works, such as Debussy, Grieg, Ravel, Saint-Saëns, Leoncavallo, Stravinski, etc.; creators of rôles, such as Van Dyck in *Werther*, Delna in *La Vivandière*, Rose Caron in *Sigurd*, Caruso in *Adrienne Lecouvreur* or *Fedora*, Lucien Fugere in *La Basoche*, Mary Garden in *Pelléas et Mélisande*. Great actors, politicians, jazz — the subjects for collection are innumerable.

Another way of collecting is assembling a diversity of makes and labels. A special category of record is that illustrated all over its face. *Photosonor* produced flexible, illustrated discs, as did *Radiola* and *Pastel*. The most varied of the illustrated productions were put out under the *Saturn* label. PATHÉ-MARCONI produced some colourful records for children under the *Lutin* label.

Various illustrated labels. The Pathé record label (note the latitude in speed!) covered the centre only of the disc, as today; the others spread over the playing surface of the entire record. They were pressed between 1931 and 1950.

A record by Bob and Bobette, decorated with motifs relating to the song.

VERTICAL RECORDING

The stylus that made the recording moved up and down, making a groove of varying depth according to the intensity of the vibration. The groove profile was known as hill-and-dale, and recordings were played by means of a rounded sapphire stylus which followed the rise and fall of the grooves.
Cylinders and discs thus recorded were known as sapphire recordings.

LATERAL RECORDING

The recording stylus vibrated from side to side in a groove of constant depth. To play such a recording, a sharp needle to follow the meanderings of the recorded track was needed.
Recordings were known as needle recordings.

SPEEDS

Cylinders
— early yellow wax   80 rpm
— black moulded, amberols   160 rpm
— dictation   80 rpm
Discs
— Pathé sapphire   80 to 120 rpm
— needle *(Gramophone)*   78 rpm (earlier examples from 70 to 78 rpm)

Souvenir

BIBLIOGRAPHY

BAUER, ROBERT, *The new Catalogue of Historical Records,* 1898-1908/9, London, Sidgwick and Jackson Ltd., 1947

BESCOBY-CHAMBERS, JOHN, *The Archives of Sound,* The Oakwood Press, 1964

BRINCOURT, MAURICE, *L'Exposition universelle de 1889,* Firmin-Didot et Cie, 1890

CARUSO, DOROTHY et GODDARD, TORRANCE, *Wings of Song,* The Story of Caruso, Minton, Balch et Company, New York, 1928

CARUSO, DOROTHY, *Enrico Caruso, his Life and Death,* Simon and Schuster, New York, 1945

CHARBON, PAUL, *Le Phonographe à la Belle Epoque,* Sodim, Bruxelles, 1977

CHARLUS, *J'ai chanté...,* Le Progrès de l'Oise, 1950

CHEW V. K., *Talking Machine,* Her Majesty's Stationery Office, 1967

CŒUROY ANDRÉ (JEAN-BELIME) et G. CLARENCE, *Le Phonographe,* Editions Kra, 1929

COPPOLA, PIERO, *Dix-sept Ans de Musique à Paris,* F. Rouge et Cie S.A., Lausanne, 1944

COSTER, MICHEL DE, *Le Disque, Art ou Affaires?,* Presses Universitaires de Grenoble, 1976

CROS, CHARLES, *Œuvres complètes,* Bibliothèque de la Pléiade, Gallimard, 1970

DESBEAUX, EMILE, *Physique populaire,* Flammarion, 1891

FAVIA-ARTSAY, AIDA, *Caruso on Records,* The Historic Record, Valhalla, New York, 1965

FIGUIER, LOUIS, *Les Grandes Inventions,* Hachette, 1896

FORD, HENRY et CROWTHER, SAMUEL, *Mon Ami Mr. Edison,* Sté Parisienne d'Edition, 1932

FORESTIER, LOUIS, *Charles Cros,* Poètes d'aujourd'hui, N° 47, Pierre Seghers, 1972

GAISBERG, FRED, W. *Music on Record,* Robert Hale, 1947

GAUTIER, EMILE, *Le Phonographe, son Passé, son Présent, son Avenir,* Flammarion, 1905 (?)

GELATT, ROLAND, *The Fabulous Phonograph,* Cassel and Company Ltd., London, 1956

GENARD, PAUL, *Cinéma d'où viens-tu?,* C.R.D.P. Lyon, 1975

GILOTAUX, PIERRE, *L'Industrie du Disque,* Que sais-je? Presses Universitaires de France, 1962

GUILBERT, YVETTE, *La Chanson de ma Vie,* Bernard Grasset, 1927

GUILBERT, YVETTE, *La Passante émerveillée,* Bernard Grasset, 1929

HEMARDINQUER, P., *Le Phonographe et ses Merveilleux Progrès,* Masson, 1930

HEMARDINQUER, PIERRE et DUMESNIL, RENÉ, *Le Livre du Disque,* Etienne Chiron, 1931

HETTINGER, PHILIPPE, *Travail et Progrès,* Librairie Commerciale, 1905

HURM, HORACE, *La Passionnante Histoire du Phonographe,* Les Publications techniques, 1944

HURST, P. G., *The Golden Age Recorded,* OAK Press, 1963

MEADOWCROFT, WILLIAM H., *Edison,* Payot, 1929

MONCEL, LE COMTE TH., DU, *Le Téléphone, le Microphone, et le Phonographe,* Bibliothèque des Merveilles, 1878

MOUCHON, JEAN-PIERRE, *Enrico Caruso, 1873-1921, sa Vie et sa Voix,* J.-P. Mouchon, 1966

NORTHROP MOORE, JERROLD, *A Voice in Time,* Hamish Hamilton, 1976

PARES, PHILIPPE, *Histoire du Droit de Reproduction mécanique,* La Compagnie du Livre, 1953

PATHÉ, CHARLES, *De Pathé Frères à Pathé Cinéma,* Collection Premier Plan, SERDOC, 1970

PETTS, LEONARD, *The Story of Nipper and the His Master's Voice Picture painted by Francis Barraud,* Talking Machine Review International, 1973

READ, OLIVER et WELCH, WALTER L., *From tin Foil to Stereo,* Howard W. Sams & Co., 2° Edition, 1976

ROSSET, THÉODORE, *Recherches expérimentales pour l'Inscription de la Voix parlée,* Armand Colin, 1911

ROUSSELET, LOUIS, *L'Exposition universelle de 1889,* Hachette et Co., 1890

VRIES, LÉONARD DE, *Les Folles Inventions du XIXe Siècle,* Editions Planètes, 1972

WEISS, EUGÈNE H., *Phonographes et Musique mécanique,* Hachette, 1930

All the machines and all the documents reproduced in the book belong to the author's collection.

PHOTOGRAPHIC CREDITS

ACKNOWLEDGEMENTS

Le Phonographe dans le Bled. — Ecoute, Fathma !.. le grand air du Prophéte.

The author wishes to thank all those who have helped him with this book particularly Mrs Marie-France Calas, Curator, and all the members of the staff of Phonothèque Nationale of the Bibliothèque Nationale, Mr Jean-Pierre Le Pavec, Director, and his helpers at the Centre culturel communal de Saint-Denis; Messrs Robert Capia, Edouard Pécourt, Georges Roussillon, Alain Vian and Bernard Gérard, Photographer.

This book was edited and produced
by Edita S.A., Lausanne
under the direction of Ami Guichard.

It was edited by Tim Chilvers, translated by D.B. Tubbs,
designed by Max Thommen, and produced
under the direction of Charles Riesen

Printed by GEA, Milan